NATURAL ENVIRONMENT RESEARCH COUNCIL

INSTITUTE OF GEOLOGICAL SCIENCES

THE GEOLOGICAL MUSEUM

9780118800047

D1796500

Geophysical Exploration

An outline of the principal methods used in the
search for minerals, oil, gas and water supplies

F W DUNNING BSc

London: Her Majesty's Stationery Office 1970

GE—A

SBN   11   880061   2

Preface

With the increasing difficulty encountered in finding workable deposits of metalliferous ore, oil, gas and water, more and more research effort and expenditure are being directed towards the development and refinement of geophysical methods of exploration. Geophysics has also benefited enormously from recent technological advances in electronic communication and computer science, and this is reflected in generally higher success rates in finding hidden ore deposits, oil and gas.

A new permanent exhibit setting out the principal methods of geophysical exploration as applied today was opened in 1968 in the Geological Museum in South Kensington. This booklet reproduces the textual and some of the visual material from the exhibit for the benefit of visitors and as a short introduction to the subject for students who have neither previous knowledge of geophysics nor a mathematical background.

Institute of Geological Sciences,
Exhibition Road,
South Kensington,
London SW7
1st October, 1969

K. C. DUNHAM
Director

Contents

Introduction

The number of workable deposits of metallic ore, oil and gas that can be discovered by ordinary surface prospecting grows steadily smaller and smaller, especially in well populated countries. Those that remain undetected are usually concealed beneath soil or other overburden and within the bedrock possibly many hundreds or thousands of feet below the surface. To sink large numbers of boreholes to locate these deposits, even on the basis of really good surface geological information, would be absurdly haphazard and uneconomic, except in areas where the underground structure is already well known from established mining operations. Geophysical exploration affords a means, at moderate cost in relation to potential returns, of either directly locating these deposits or of determining the subsurface structure so that exploratory drilling can be restricted to favourable areas.

Fig. 1 is an idealized section of the crust showing the shapes of some bodies of valuable metallic ore and structures of the type in which oil and gas may accumulate. The scale has necessarily been distorted; the orebodies are much larger in relation to the oil accumulations than they would normally be. Also, the shapes of the orebodies should not be taken as characteristic; orebodies may assume various shapes, though tabular masses and lenses, gently or steeply inclined, predominate, and many valuable sources of base metal consist of large volumes of rock throughout which the ore minerals are dispersed.

The section also shows the two main types of geological structure encountered by geologists and geophysicists: gently folded and geologically young *platform* sedimentary rocks in which most oil accumulations are found, and the older, often highly deformed and metamorphosed *orogenic* sedimentary and igneous rocks in which many metallic orebodies occur, collectively termed the *basement*.

Geophysical exploration is really an assortment of methods utilizing physical principles to enable the prospector to 'see' underground and is based on the fact that rocks and minerals of different types may display large differences in certain physical properties:

1

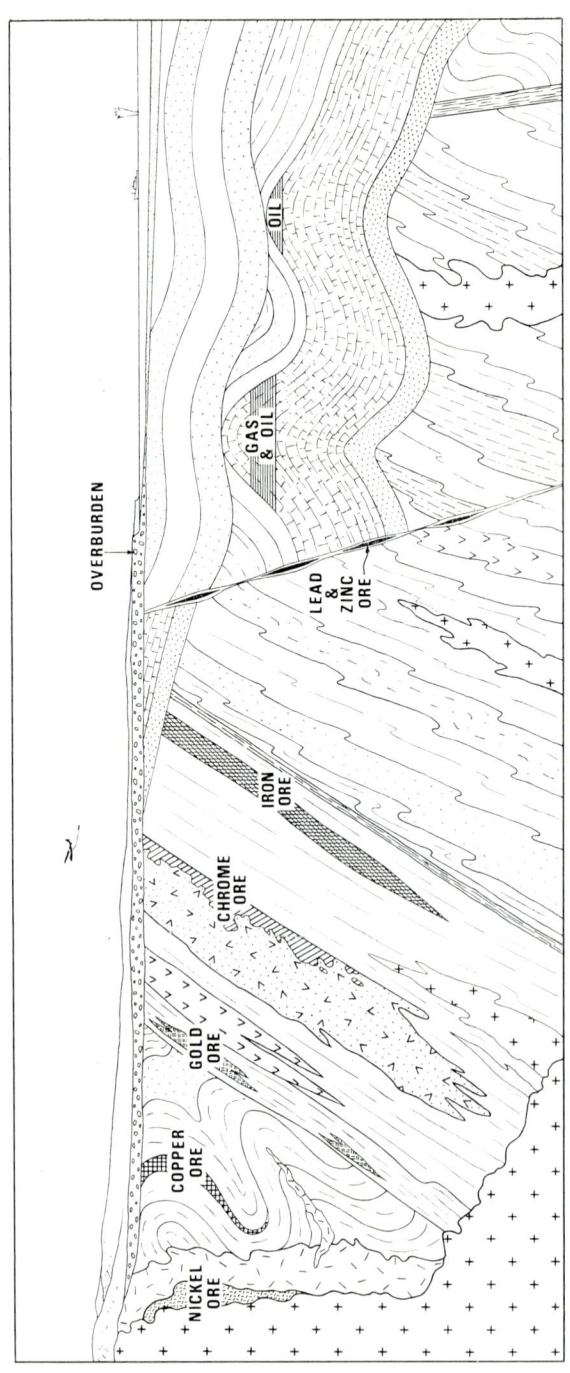

Figure 1. Idealized cross-section of the Earth's crust showing the forms of some common metallic orebodies, oil and gas accumulations and the geological structures with which they are associated.

2

ELASTICITY (which determines the speed of seismic waves)

DENSITY (which affects the strength of the Earth's gravity field)

MAGNETIZATION (which affects the strength of the Earth's magnetic field)

ELECTRICAL CHARACTERISTICS

NATURAL RADIOACTIVITY LEVELS

Consequently an area made up of rock formations showing pronounced contrasts in these properties or containing ore deposits in which they are markedly enhanced will display significant variations from place to place when these properties or their interactions with other physical stimuli, natural or artificial, are measured, recorded and collated. These variations will be distributed in a pattern directly related to the disposition of the causative rock or mineral formations. The physical properties listed above form the basis of the five principal methods of geophysical exploration:

SEISMIC REFLECTION AND REFRACTION

GRAVITY

MAGNETIC

ELECTRICAL AND ELECTROMAGNETIC

RADIOMETRIC

Though primarily employed at the surface and on occasion in underground workings, these methods have also been adapted for use in boreholes to provide supplementary data for other geological and geophysical studies. In oil and gas exploration, the seismic reflection method is by far the most widely used, with gravity, seismic refraction and magnetic methods following in that order. Regional reconnaissance surveys using the last three methods may, if promising, be followed up by more detailed seismic reflection work. In mineral exploration, the magnetic, electrical and electromagnetic and radiometric methods are most commonly used. The five principal methods and their main applications are summarized in the table on the following two pages.

3

METHOD	FIELD OPERATIONS	QUANTITIES MEASURED
SEISMIC	Reflection and refraction surveys using, on land, large 10–20 man crews in several trucks with seismic energy sources of various types, detector arrays and recording equipment and, at sea, one or two ships. Complex data-processing equipment in central office. Small 2–man refraction team using a sledgehammer energy source	Time for seismic waves to return to surface after reflection or refraction by subsurface formations
GRAVITY	Land surveys using gravity meters, 2 men per meter. Marine surveys using gravity meters on stabilized platforms or submersible meters	Variations in the strength of the Earth's gravity field
MAGNETIC	Airborne and marine magnetic surveys using magnetometers of various types. Ground magnetic surveys using small teams of 2 men per magnetometer	Variations in the strength of the Earth's magnetic field
ELECTRICAL AND ELECTRO-MAGNETIC	Ground self-potential and resistivity surveys, ground and airborne electromagnetic surveys, induced polarization surveys. Teams of 2–6 men	Natural potentials, potential drop between electrodes, natural and induced electromagnetic fields and induced overvoltages.
RADIOMETRIC	Ground and airborne surveys using scintillation counters and gamma-ray spectrometers, ground surveys using Geiger counters. Team of 1–4 men	Natural radioactivity levels of rocks and minerals, induced radioactivity
BOREHOLE LOGGING	Seismic, gravity, magnetic, electrical and radiometric measurements using specially developed equipment lowered into the borehole. Team of 1–4 men	Speeds of seismic waves, vertical variations in the gravity and magnetic field, apparent resistivities, self-potentials, overvoltages, natural and induced radioactivity

DERIVED OR COMPUTED RESULTS	PRINCIPAL APPLICATIONS
Depths to reflecting and refracting formations in the shape of seismic time-sections and seismic depth-sections, speeds of seismic waves, seismic contour maps	Exploration for oil and gas, regional geological studies
	Superficial deposit surveys, site investigation for engineering projects
Bouguer Anomaly and residual gravity maps and profiles; depths to rocks of contrasting density	Reconnaissance exploration for oil and gas, regional and detailed geological studies
Aeromagnetic and marine magnetic maps, magnetic profiles; depths to rocks or minerals of contrasting magnetization	Reconnaissance exploration for oil and gas, search for mineral deposits, regional and detailed geological studies
Anomaly maps and profiles, position and form of orebodies, depths to rock layers of contrasting resistivity	Exploration for minerals; site investigation
Airborne isorad maps, radiometric anomalies, location and quality of radioactive and other mineral deposits	Exploration for metals used in atomic energy plant
Continuous velocity logs; resistivities and thicknesses of beds; densities; gas and oil content; potassium, thorium and uranium content; salinities of water	Discovery and evaluation of oil, gas and water supplies, regional geological studies by borehole correlation as an adjunct to seismic and other types of geophysical and geological survey, seismic velocity data for seismic depth-sections

Seismic Methods

Though expensive, seismic methods provide more and better structural information than other geophysical methods in areas suited to their use.

Basic Principles

The sudden release of energy from, for example, the detonation of an explosive charge in the ground or mechanical pounding of the ground surface, generates *seismic shock waves*—in effect a rapidly travelling series of compressions and rarefactions of the rock—which move out in hemispherical wave-fronts from the point of energy release.

The speed at which these seismic waves travel is mainly dependent on the *elasticity* of the rocks; it tends to be low in uncompacted clays and sands and high in igneous and the older indurated sedimentary rocks. When, after passing through 'low-speed' rocks, the seismic wave-fronts encounter the upper surface of a 'high-speed' rock formation, some energy is *reflected* directly back to the surface while the remainder is *refracted* into the high-speed formation. One ray of this refracted energy which has approached the high-speed formation at the so-called 'critical angle' travels in the high-speed formation along its upper boundary. The material at the boundary is thereby subjected to oscillating stress from below; this generates new disturbances along the boundary which travel upwards through the low-speed rocks and eventually reach the surface. Reflected seismic waves—but not refracted waves—may also reach the surface from the *lower* boundary of a high-speed formation.

Fig. 2 shows the paths of seismic waves which have reached the surface again after reflection and refraction on encountering a high-speed formation at depth. Measurement of the time taken for such reflected and refracted waves to reach detector arrays at the surface is the basis of the two main methods of seismic exploration, seismic reflection and seismic refraction.

THE SEISMIC REFLECTION METHOD

In this, the most extensively used of all geophysical methods, the detectors are placed relatively close to the explosion point to exclude refracted waves. The depths to the reflecting layers and their dips can be computed, knowing the speeds of seismic waves in the rock formations, from the times taken to travel from the explosion point to the reflecting layers and back again to groups of detectors at the surface. The method is thus analogous to echo-sounding at sea.

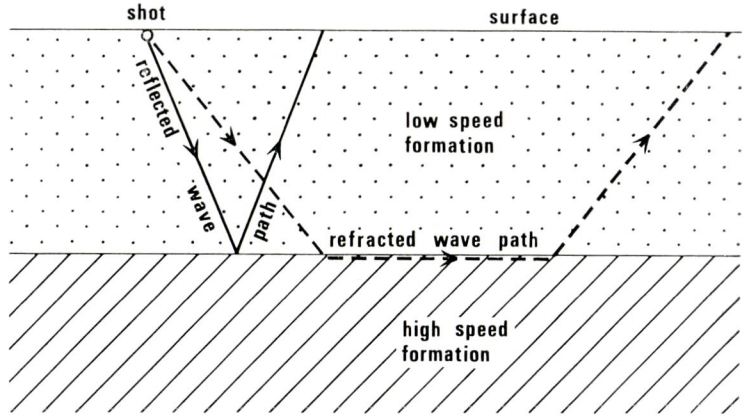

Figure 2. Ray paths of seismic waves reflected and refracted on encountering upper boundary of 'high-speed' formation at depth. Reflected ray is one of infinite number radiating in all directions from shot-point. Refracted ray is one that has approached boundary at 'critical angle'; other refracted rays traverse 'high-speed' formation without returning to surface.

THE SEISMIC REFRACTION METHOD

In the simple case of refraction by a single high-speed formation at depth, the travel-times for the seismic wave which proceeds *directly* from the shot-point to detectors placed on a straight line through the shot-point (S to G_0-G_1-G_2 in Fig. 3) and the travel times for the first *refracted* wave to arrive at the detectors (S to AB_1G_1, AB_2G_2, AB_3G_3) are plotted on a graph against shot-detector distances (SG_0, SG_1, SG_2, SG_3). The depth 'h' to the high-speed formation can be calculated from the graph using the formula $h = \frac{1}{2} \sqrt{\dfrac{V_1 - V_0}{V_1 + V_0}} \; x_c$ where V_0 and V_1 are the speeds of the seismic waves in the low-speed and high-speed formations respectively and x_c is the distance to the point where direct and refracted waves arrive simultaneously. The method works equally

7

well for multi-layered rock sequences provided that each layer is sufficiently thick and transmits seismic waves at higher speeds than the one above it; the time-distance curve (Fig. 3) simply has more segments.

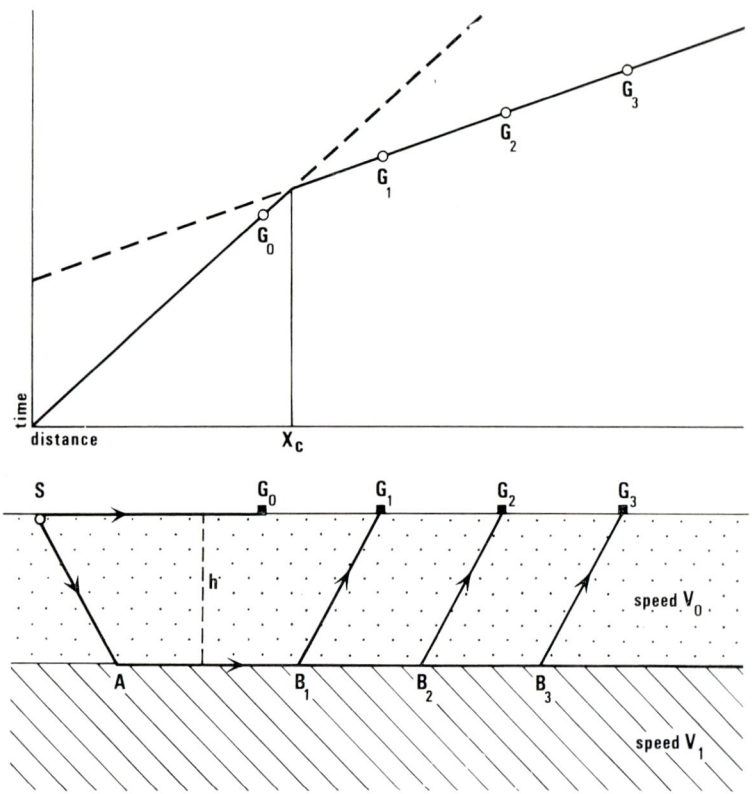

Figure 3. Ray paths of refracted seismic waves arriving first at geophones and, *above*, time-distance plot of direct and refracted waves.

The dip (inclination to the horizontal) of the high-speed layer and the position of faults or fractures which displace the layer can also be estimated from the time-distance graphs. Refraction surveys also provide data on the speed of seismic waves in specific rock formations.

8

Equipment and Instruments

Explosives are still the most widely used energy source. In operations on land, the explosive charges are placed in shot-holes drilled to depths of 25 to 250 feet by a truck-mounted drilling rig. In operations at sea, the charge is run out on the end of a firing line or floated on a balloon. In the recently developed *Geoseis* system, the explosive is a length of detonating fuse buried to a depth of 1 to 2 feet by means of a plough device towed by a tractor. Apart from its cheapness, greater efficiency and safety, this has the advantage that the energy can be directionally controlled. *Aquaseis* is a comparable marine system in which lengths of detonating fuse are exploded underwater.

A variety of new energy sources less hazardous than explosives has appeared in recent years. Fig. 4 shows three systems in which the energy is applied to the ground surface. *Vibroseis* is an electro-mechanical device (shown here in its land adaptation) which vibrates the surface at selected frequencies. *Dinoseis* employs a gas-propelled piston which strikes the ground. It is shown here mounted in a heavy earthmoving truck for land use; at sea it is lowered to the sea bed from a barge. In small-scale seismic refraction techniques used in site investigation for engineering projects, the seismic energy is produced by placing a steel plate on the ground and striking it with a *sledgehammer* connected electrically with the portable recording unit. The *air gun* (Fig. 4) is a marine energy source which generates a seismic pulse by suddenly releasing highly compressed air into the water from the ports of the gun. The frequency range of the seismic pulse can be controlled by firing simultaneously an array of 24 guns of differing compression-chamber capacities. Two other marine energy sources, towed behind the ship in a continuous-profiling technique used mostly where only shallow depth penetration is required, are the '*sparker*', an electric arc discharge device, and the '*boomer*', an electromechanical sound source in which an aluminium plate is violently repelled from a copper coil energized (as is the 'sparker') by a capacitor bank.

DETECTION AND RECORDING EQUIPMENT

The reflected and refracted seismic waves are detected by *geophones* in which the seismic vibrations are converted into oscillating electrical signals by a coil and moving magnet or by a pressure-sensitive piezo-

Left: Vibroseis: the ground is vibrated at selected frequencies by an electro-mechanical vibrator; the return signal is cross-correlated with the outgoing vibrations.

Seismograph Service Limited

Centre left: Dinoseis: the ground surface is struck by a piston impelled by the explosion of a propane-oxygen mixture. The Dinoseis gas gun is shown here mounted in an earthmoving truck.

Geo Space Corporation

Bottom left: Sledgehammer and steel plate: for shallow refraction surveys sufficient energy is generated by striking a steel plate (placed on the ground) with a sledgehammer electrically connected to the recording apparatus (in the foreground). *IGS photo*

Below: Explosives: a 4000-lb shot fired in a seismic refraction survey in northern Iraq. The smoke in the left-hand corner is from a detonator fired together with the main charge to record the instant of explosion. *British Petroleum Co. Ltd.*

Figure 4. Seismic Energy Sources

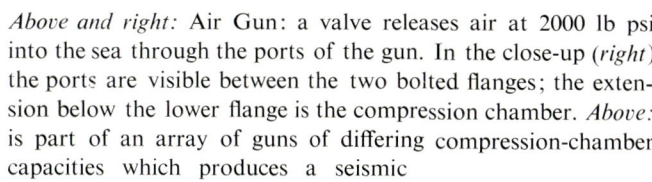

Above and right: Air Gun: a valve releases air at 2000 lb psi into the sea through the ports of the gun. In the close-up (*right*) the ports are visible between the two bolted flanges; the extension below the lower flange is the compression chamber. *Above:* is part of an array of guns of differing compression-chamber capacities which produces a seismic pulse of controlled frequency range.

Geophysical Service International Ltd.

Right: Sparker: an electric arc discharge device in which a heavy current at very high voltage from a capacitor bank produces a spark across concentric electrodes immersed in the water. The spark vaporizes the water producing a pulsating plasma bubble. The 'sparker' is shown here being lowered into the water.

Hunting Geology and Geophysics Ltd.

11

Figure 5. Attaching geophones to the cable from the recording truck.
Geophysical Service International Ltd.

electric crystal detector. Geophones on land are pressed into the ground
(Fig. 5); at sea they are either placed on the sea bottom, suspended
from floats or strung out in a buoyant cable up to a mile and a half in
length towed at a depth of 40 feet (Fig. 6). The signals from the geophones are selectively amplified to improve weak returns, filtered to
exclude various unwanted frequencies, and fed into recording apparatus
mounted in a recording truck (Fig. 7) or in the ship. Older recording
systems and those for shallow refraction work use a 'seismic camera'
which yields a record on photographic paper consisting of parallel rows
of 'wiggly' lines. Each line is produced by a beam of light from a
moving-coil galvanometer connected through to a single geophone or
group of geophones. The moment of arrival of a reflected or refracted
seismic wave is shown on the record by a 'kick'—a high peak and trough
—amongst the background 'noise' of lower peaks and troughs produced
by scattering and diffraction of the seismic energy (Fig. 8). More modern
recording systems produce 'analogue' records on magnetic tape; such
systems usually have facilities for tape playback giving a 'wiggly'-line
paper record. Large-scale seismic operations today, such as those in the

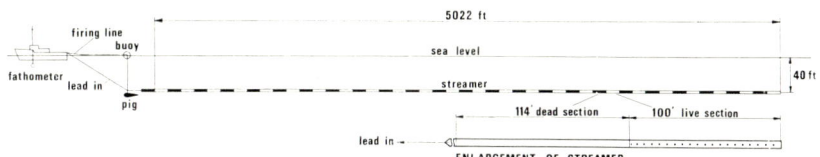

firing line
buoy
fathometer
lead in
pig
5022 ft
sea level
streamer
40 ft
114' dead section
100' live section
lead in
ENLARGEMENT OF STREAMER

Figure 6. A 1600-metre marine geophone streamer used in multiple common depth-point (CDP) reflection surveys. Streamer is buoyant polythene tube filled with kerosene and towed at depth of 40 feet; it comprises 24 live sections, each containing 20 piezoelectric crystal geophones electrically linked to give one signal trace on the seismic record. *Geophysical Service International Ltd.*

North Sea, use field digital recording systems which yield digital magnetic tape records for processing in a digital computer. In digital recording, the signal from the geophones is read at millisecond intervals and recorded as binary digits across the width of the tape, whereas in ordinary 'analogue' tape the signals are recorded in variably magnetized tracks along the length of the tape. In all three recording systems, time lines or impulses, including one for the instant of explosion, are impressed on the paper or magnetic tape record.

Figure 7. Interior of recording truck equipped with digital recording apparatus.
IGS photo

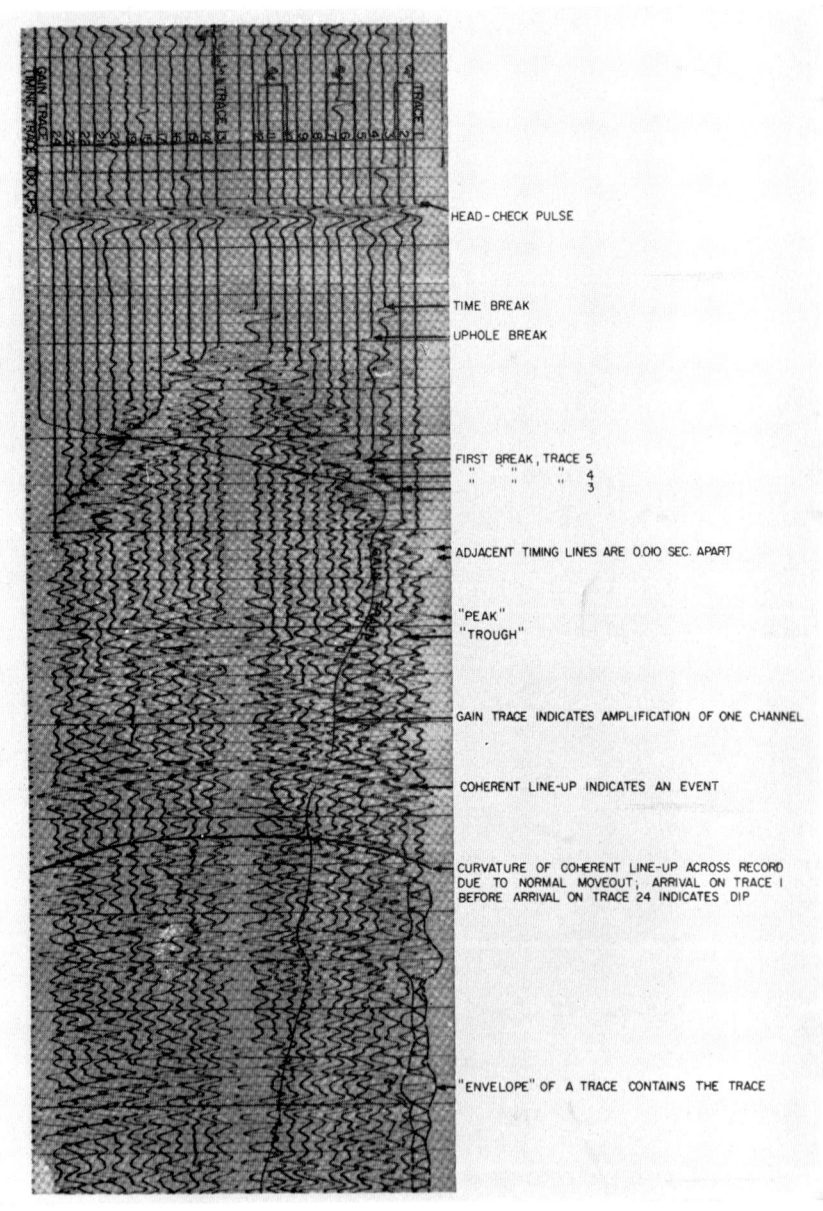

Figure 8. 'Wiggle'-trace seismic record.

(R. E. Sheriff, *Geophysics*, 1968, Vol. 33, Soc. Explor. Geophysicists)

In continuous-profile marine 'sparker' and 'boomer' reflection surveys, the return signal from a single crystal geophone or linked geophone array towed ahead of the 'sparker' or 'boomer' is recorded by a 'flying-spot' facsimile-type depth recorder, which produces an 'echogram' paper record (Fig. 12) and also triggers the 'sparker' or 'boomer'.

Field Operations

Seismic exploration parties (Fig. 9) are sent into areas considered promising from reconnaissance by less expensive geophysical methods such as gravity and magnetic surveying and from geological studies. An average seismic reflection party for land operations comprises 15 to 20 men; refraction parties can be twice as large.

The selected area is visited first by a survey party who accurately locate the shot-hole and recording positions. Drilling crews move in to drill the shot-holes, followed by the shooter who loads the hole with

Figure 9. Seismic reflection and gravity field parties: *foreground*, surveyors and gravity crew equipped with 'Worden' gravity meters; *left background*, seismic recording truck with, in front, magnetic tape recording apparatus; *centre background*, survey party for shot-hole and geophone location; *right background*, drilling rigs; *right foreground*, shooter with firing apparatus. *Geophysical Service International*

explosive while the recording crew lay out the cable and attach the geo-phones at predetermined intervals. At sea, the ship (or ships) firing the charges and/or towing the detector array use radionavigation devices for accurate position location. When the geophone circuit has been tested and the recording apparatus started, the shot is fired, as a rule automatically by a signal from the recording apparatus. Radio-communication is necessary in seismic refraction work where the shot-hole and the geophone array may be several miles apart.

SHOT-DETECTOR LAYOUT

Seismic reflection: A common arrangement of shot-points and geo-phones for continuous coverage on land is the *split-spread* layout, shown in Fig. 10. Geophones are grouped on either side of the shot-point B; after the shot is fired, the geophones between A and B are leap-frogged to the other side of C for the second shot from C. The geophones are usually spaced at calculated intervals and the signals from individual geophones or groups of geophones mixed to cancel out interference from horizontal ground motion. A modern technique which gives a clearer picture of subsurface structure and is used in conjunction with digital recording and computer processing is *multiple common depth-point coverage* (CDP). In this, reflections from the same reflecting point on a subsurface formation boundary are obtained, for example, six times over by moving on the shot-detector array one-twelfth of its

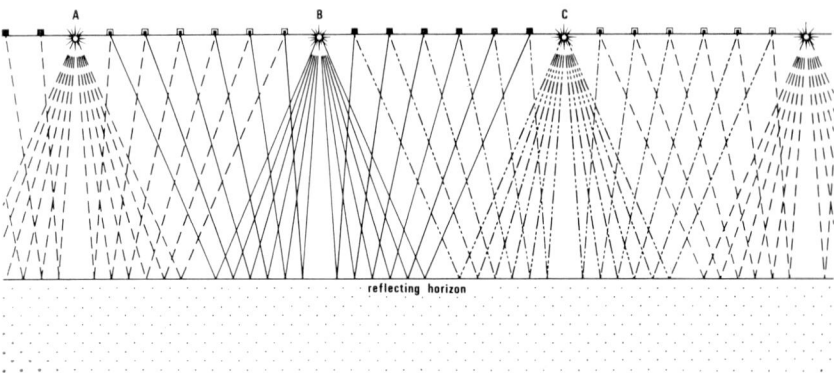

Figure 10. 'Split-spread' shotpoint-geophone arrangement used in continuous-coverage reflection shooting.

16

length for each shot (Fig. 11). At sea, the geophone streamer is simply towed along the requisite amount; on land, geophones are removed from one end of the array and added to the other. Compounding or 'stacking' of the corrected traces from each shot emphasizes primary reflections and attenuates 'noise' such as multiple reflections and refractions.

Seismic refraction: The most common arrangement in refraction work is *profile shooting*. Shot-points and geophones are laid out on long lines, with a row of geophones receiving refracted waves from shots fired successively at a predetermined distance from either end of the geophone array, the whole process being repeated at uniform intervals down the line. Other refraction techniques are *broadside shooting*, in which a central line of geophones is flanked by parallel lines of shot-points, the lines running perpendicular to the regional trend of rock formations; and *fan-shooting*, in which geophones are placed along a sector of a

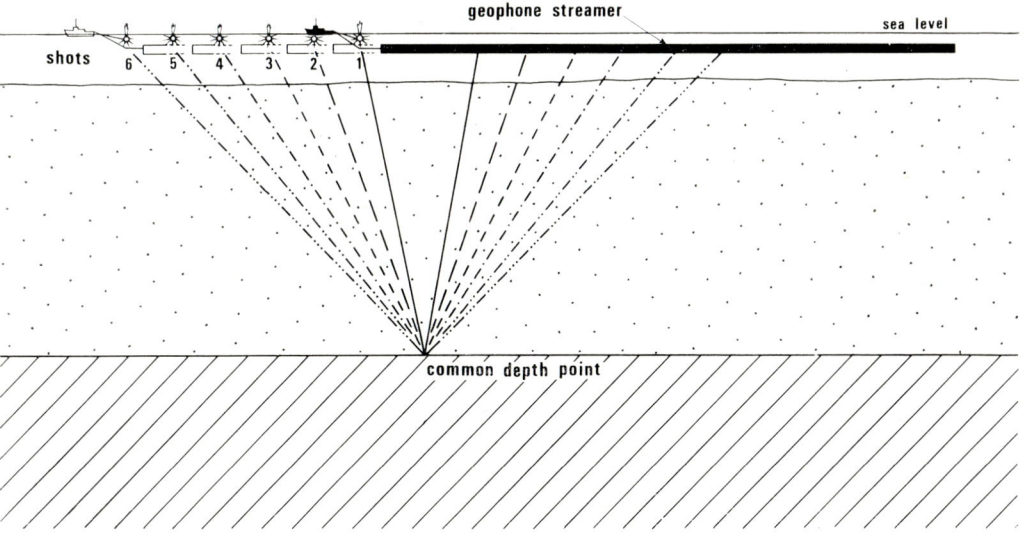

Figure 11. Multiple common depth-point coverage at sea: streamer is moved on one twelfth of its length for each shot: reflections reaching successively more distant parts of geophone streamer are obtained six times over from same point on sub-surface formation boundary. 'Stacking' of corrected traces recording same reflection boosts in-phase reflection signal and attenuates out-of-phase 'noise'.

17

curve of some 5 to 10 miles radius with the shot-point situated at the centre of curvature, a second 'fan' being shot at right-angles to the first whenever that showed the presence of high-speed formations such as rock-salt. Many oil-bearing salt-domes were found by this method in the early days of seismic prospecting.

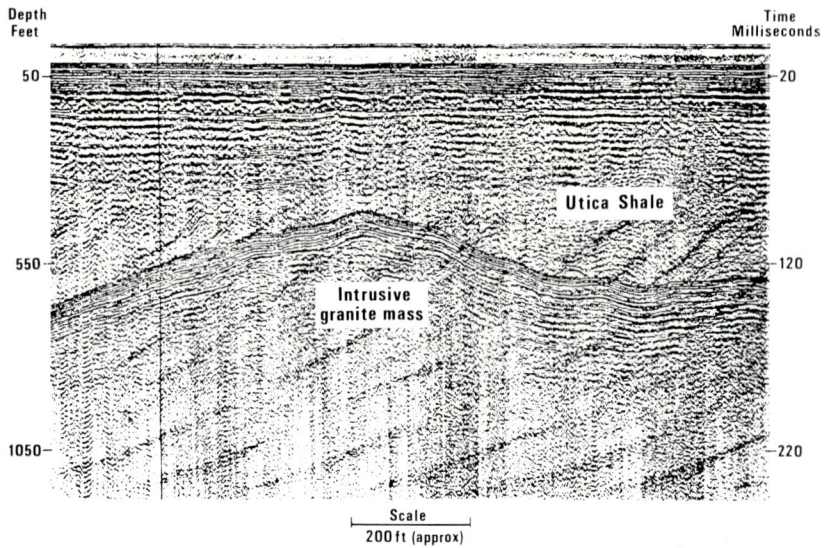

Figure 12. 'Echogram'-type seismic record from 'sparker' survey. *Huntec Ltd.*

Data Processing and Geological Interpretation

The products of the operations so far described are 'wiggly'-line and 'echogram' paper records and analogue and digital magnetic tape records. The 'wiggly'-line records are mainly used for monitoring purposes and, in refraction work, for the preparation of time-distance curves and profiles. Magnetic tape records from continuous-coverage reflection shooting are corrected for elevation, weathering and 'normal moveout' (the increasing length of seismic wave-paths to increasingly distant geophones) and the playback 'wiggly'-line records placed edge-to-edge to make 'record sections'. Correlation of reflections from one record to the next in these sections is facilitated by blacking in the crests of the 'wiggles'. The 'echogram' records from 'sparker' and

18

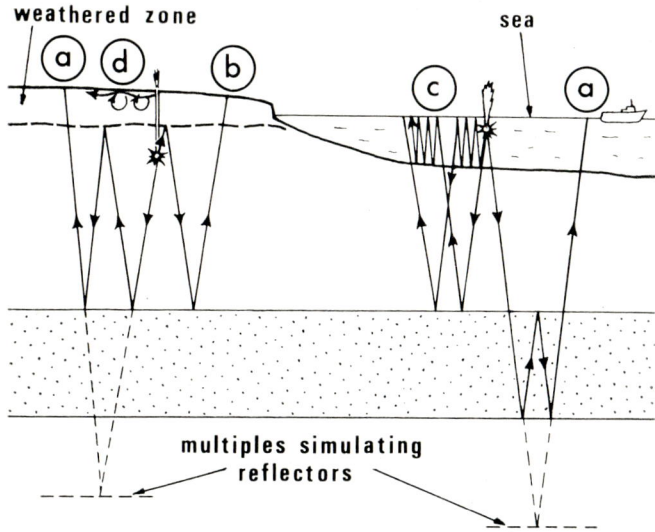

Figure 13. Some obscuring effects in seismic reflection shooting: (*a*) multiples, (*b*) ghosts, (*c*) water reverberations, (*d*) ground roll. Signal distortions caused by such effects are minimized by shooting techniques such as CDP with horizontal 'stacking' in conjunction with digital processing.

Figure 14. Seismic digital playback unit with oscilloscope display for monitoring seismic records processed in a digital computer. *IGS photo*

19

'boomer' surveys (Fig. 12) are in effect seismic record sections comprising juxtaposed single-trace seismic records showing reflections both from the sea bed and from sub-bottom reflecting layers. Digital magnetic tape records from multiple common depth-point shooting are fed into a special high-speed computer programmed to perform complex running calculations on the digitized signal. These calculations, based on communication theory, are designed to bring up weak reflections and attenuate extraneous 'noise', multiple reflections, water reverberations and other obscuring effects (Fig. 13). The computer and playback-plotter unit (Fig. 14) produce a seismic record section (Fig. 15) on which geological formation boundaries can be recognized and marked and which differs from a normal geological section in that vertical distances are

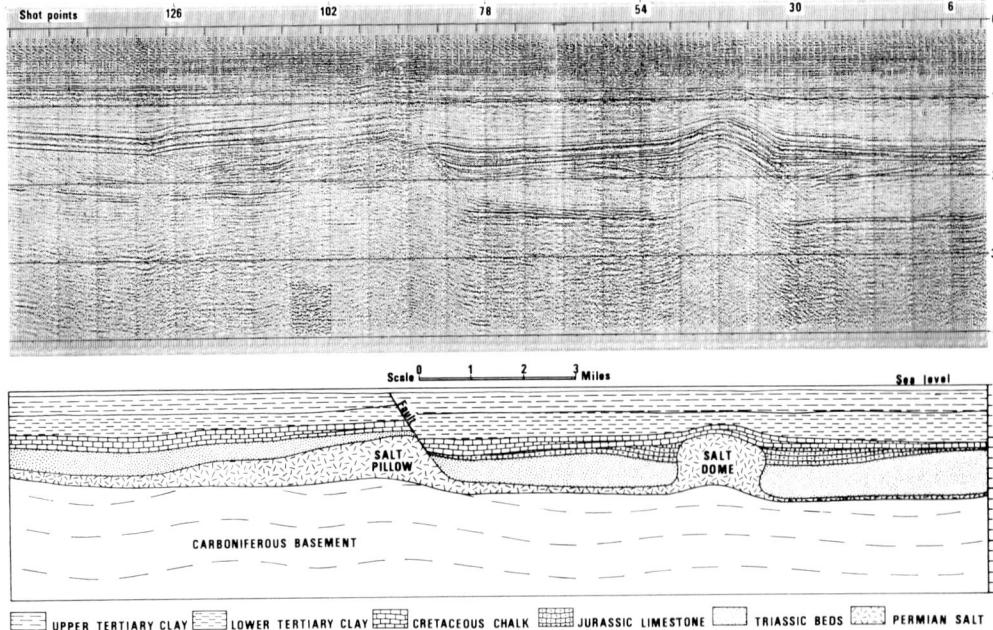

Figure 15. *Above:* Seismic time-section from North Sea obtained by 6-fold multiple common depth-point coverage using digital recording and processing.
Below: Seismic depth-section obtained by computer analysis of time-section above. Geological formations thought responsible for reflections are inserted on evidence from boreholes in adjacent areas. *Geophysical Service International Ltd.*

20

expressed in terms of time only. Where necessary, these time-sections can be converted to depth-sections (Fig. 15). For this a good knowledge of the speeds of seismic waves in the relevant geological formations is needed; this is obtained from determinations made in existing boreholes, from specialized seismic shooting and by the recently developed application of computerized analytical techniques to the digital field record.

Seismic sections and velocity data are used, together with other geological information from borehole logs and surface observations, to draw contour maps and sections showing depths to geological horizons. With the aid of such maps and sections the oil geologist can identify structures which might have trapped oil or gas and suggest sites for exploratory boreholes.

Gravity Methods

Gravity methods are mainly used in regional reconnaissance surveys to reveal anomalies which may be investigated later by other geological and geophysical methods.

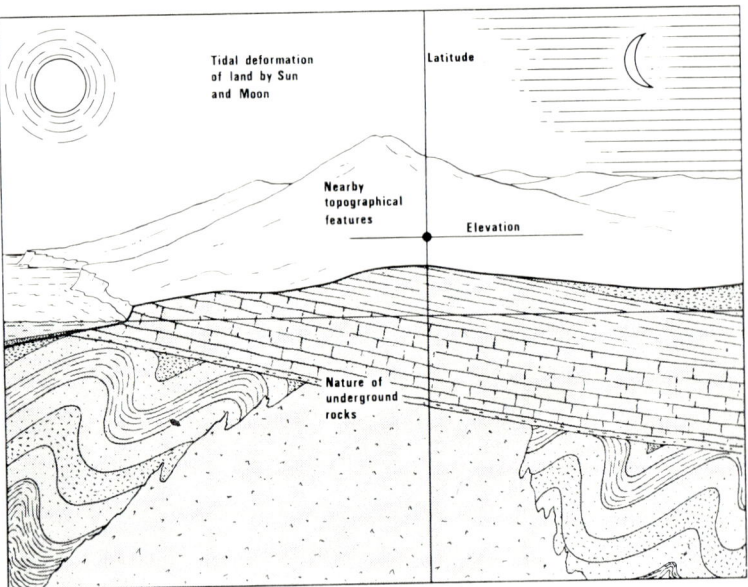

Figure 16. Factors affecting the Earth's gravity field at any particular place.

Basic Principles

The Earth's gravity field is not constant everywhere but shows small variations from place to place. At any particular locality, the magnitude of the force of gravity (measured as the acceleration due to gravity, that is, the rate of increase in velocity of a falling body) is influenced by the following factors (Fig. 16):

1. Variation in the gravitational attraction of the Earth according to the latitude of the locality
2. The elevation of the locality above sea-level

3. The effects of nearby topographical features
4. Tidal deformation of the Earth's crust by the gravitational attraction of the Sun and Moon
5. Variations in the nature and density of underground rocks in the vicinity.

The aim of gravity surveys is to measure very precisely the variations in the acceleration due to gravity throughout an area and then to eliminate factors 1 to 4 so that only variations due to geological causes are left.

Equipment and Instruments

The unit of measurement of acceleration is called in geophysics the *gal* (in honour of Galileo), which is an acceleration (increase in velocity) of 1 centimetre-per-second per second. The acceleration due to gravity at the Earth's surface is about 980 gals, but the variations in gravity that are of interest to geophysicists are extremely small, of the order of 1 ten-thousandth of a gal. The practical unit of measurement is therefore the *milligal*, 1 thousandth of a gal.

Modern gravity meters used in exploration measure not the full or *absolute* value of the acceleration due to gravity but the small *differences* in this value between one place and the next. The modern temperature-compensated lightweight gravity meter shown in Fig. 17 is the 'Worden' gravity meter which weighs only 6 lb. and has an accuracy of 0.01 milligal. The basic mechanism (Fig. 18) is made entirely of fused quartz. An arm A with weight W is supported by a spring S acting through a second angled arm. The countering pull of the spring is progressively decreased as the weighted arm is pulled down by gravity, thus magnifying the effect of gravity alone. The instrument is read by noting the amount of adjustment required to cancel the displacement of the spring, the reading on the adjustment screw being multiplied by a calibration factor to convert it to milligals.

In land surveys the gravity meter is carried in a light truck, by helicopter alighting for readings, and in marsh country, by small boats or buoyant vehicles known as marsh buggies. Lightweight meters can be transported on foot in inaccessible areas. At sea the gravity meter is

23

mounted on a stabilized platform, suspended in gimbals or lowered to the sea bed in a watertight case and operated by remote control.

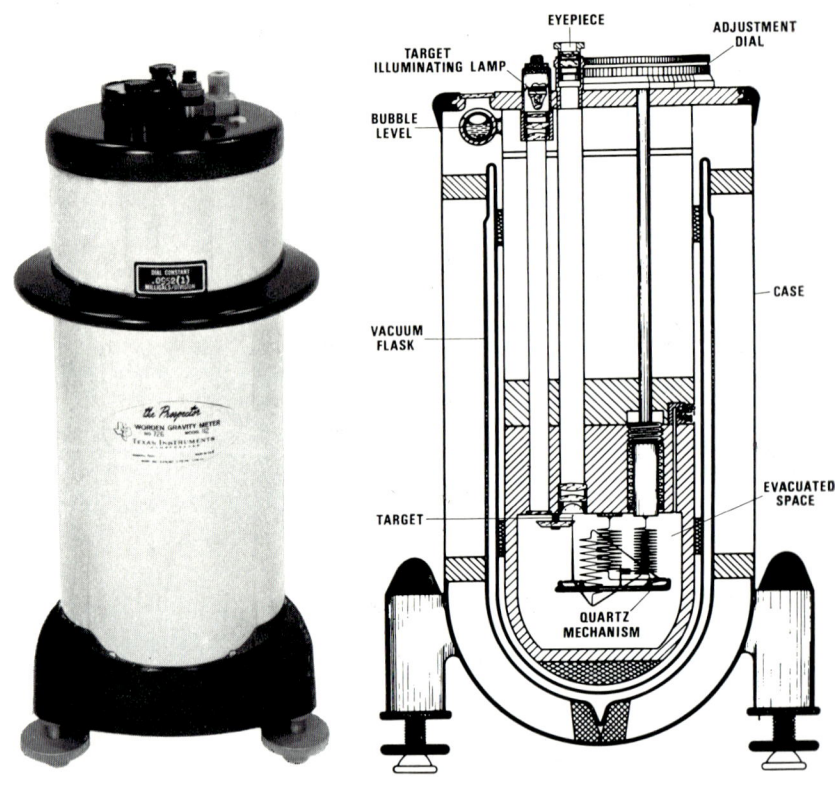

Figure 17. 'Worden' gravity meter and, *right*, cross-section.

Texas Instruments Inc.

Field Operations and Data Processing

FIELD OPERATIONS

The object of the field gravity survey is to acquire the data necessary to produce gravity maps and profiles. The location and spacing of points or 'stations' at which gravity measurements are to be taken is decided beforehand, and depends on the type of survey required. For regional

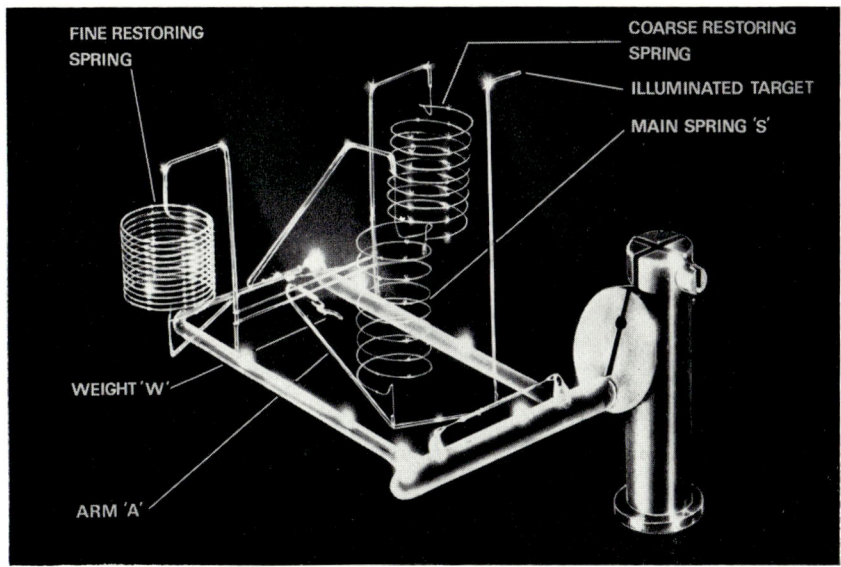

FINE RESTORING SPRING

COARSE RESTORING SPRING

ILLUMINATED TARGET

MAIN SPRING 'S'

WEIGHT 'W'

ARM 'A'

Figure 18. Basic mechanism of the 'Worden' gravity meter.

Texas Instruments Inc.

reconnaissance surveys, stations may be located at $\frac{1}{2}$ mile or 1 mile intervals either on map grid intersections or at points along roads; for more detailed work, such as delineation of orebodies, spacings may be as small as 20 yards.

Because gravity differences large enough to be of geological significance are produced by changes in elevation of a few inches and of only 100 feet in north-south distance, the location and elevation of stations must be established with very high precision. For regional surveys in Britain, locations and bench-mark elevations from six-inch maps are sufficiently accurate; in less well mapped areas, a survey party, which precedes the gravity meter crew, marks the station locations. The gravity survey of an area is conducted from a local base station at which the value of the acceleration due to gravity is known with reference to a fundamental base where the acceleration due to gravity has been accurately measured by the pendulum method. Fig. 19 shows the relation between the fundamental base, the local base and the field stations.

Owing to the slow creep of the springs or torsion fibres in most types of gravity meter, the readings during the course of a day will vary by a significant amount. To determine and allow for this instrument 'drift', readings are taken at the same station twice or more during the day, a 'drift' curve is plotted and the correction applied to all intermediate readings. The 'drift' correction also takes account of the diurnal variation caused by the tidal gravitational attraction of the Sun and Moon.

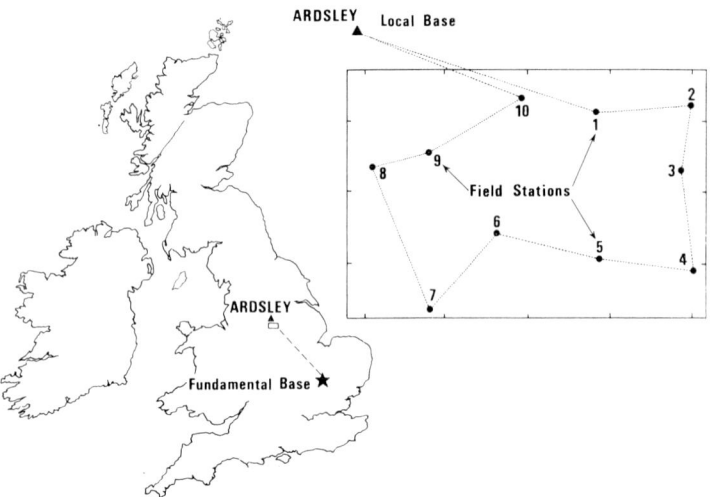

Figure 19. Gravity surveying: relationship between fundamental base (Cambridge), local base (Ardsley) and field stations.

DATA PROCESSING

To establish from the raw field data the increment of gravity due solely to variations in rock density distribution, it is necessary to apply various corrections to the field data. These are for the elevation of the station above a datum plane (which may or may not be sea level), for gross topographical features in the vicinity of the station, for geographical latitude and, if not already incorporated in the drift correction, for Earth-tides.

The increment obtained after these corrections have been made, and which is plotted on gravity maps and profiles, is called the *Bouguer Anomaly*.

26

The Bouguer Anomaly equals therefore:
Gravity observed at the station
    minus
The theoretical sea-level value of gravity at the station
    plus
The elevation correction
    plus
The topographical or terrain correction (if any).

The *gravity observed at the station* is the known gravity value at the local base plus the reading on the gravity meter. The *theoretical value of the gravity at the station* is obtained by interpolation from tables giving the values calculated from the International Gravity Formula for all latitudes. The *elevation correction* (Fig. 20), which reduces all readings to what they would be if all stations were at the same level or datum plane, consists of two parts: (a) the 'free-air' correction which takes count of the lessening pull of gravity at increasing distances from the Earth's centre, and (b) the 'Bouguer' correction which removes the gravitational pull of the rock between the station and the datum plane.

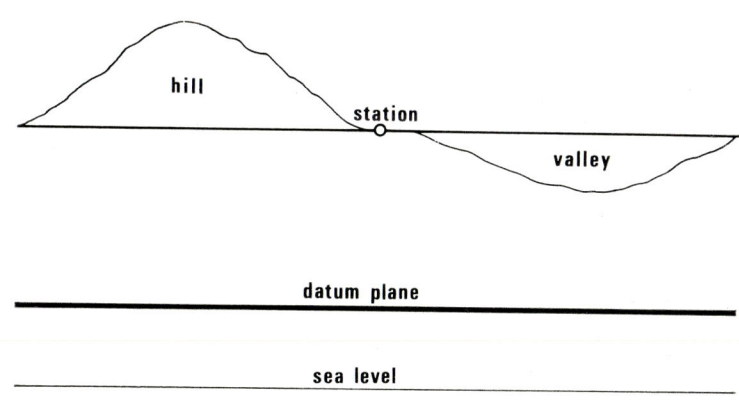

Figure 20. Elevation and terrain corrections: elevation correction (*a*) takes count of reduction in gravity at height of station above datum (free-air correction) and (*b*) removes gravitational pull of rock between station and datum (Bouguer correction). Terrain correction compensates for reduction in gravity at station caused by upward pull of hill and adds for valley not allowed for in Bouguer correction.

In the *terrain correction* (Fig. 20), the reduction in gravity at the station caused by the upward gravitational pull of hills is compensated for, and an addition is made in respect of valleys which had not been allowed for in the Bouguer correction. The Bouguer and terrain corrections both require a knowledge of the average density of the surface rocks in the area; this is obtained from tables, laboratory tests on samples and from borehole logging.

The values of the Bouguer Anomaly calculated for each station are plotted on a map and contoured at suitable intervals. Such gravity maps are the basis for subsequent operations designed to sharpen up the anomalies caused by structures of likely geological and commercial interest.

RESIDUAL GRAVITY MAPS

In many areas judged suitable for gravity survey, superficial strata disposed in comparatively simple structures overlie a denser basement of complex internal structure. Gravity effects due to local structures in the superficial strata may be partly obscured or distorted by regional gravity effects caused by large-scale basement structures. The regional, deep-seated gravity effects can be removed or minimized to produce a *residual gravity map* showing only the effects of shallow structures which are usually of greater commercial interest. In the gravity map in Fig. 21, the east-west contours represent a regional gravity gradient attributed to the basement. The distortion or anomaly in the centre of the map is assumed to be caused by a local shallow structure. The regional gravity contours can be projected across the anomaly, and the differences at their intersections with the actual contours can themselves be contoured, to give a residual gravity map showing an anomaly due solely to the shallow structure. A similar subtraction of regional gravity can be performed on gravity profiles. Residual gravity may also be derived from gravity maps by analytical methods in which the average of gravity at regular points around circles superimposed on the map is subtracted from the observed gravity at the centres of the circles. In *second-derivative* maps, on which the vertical rate of change of the gravity gradient is plotted and contoured, the gravity effects of smaller, shallower structures are magnified at the expense of larger, deeper structures. The second derivatives are computed from special charts superimposed on the gravity map, using a method of averaging around circles similar to that used for residual gravity maps. It is also possible to compute the gravity field at horizontal surfaces above or below that of the actual observed field, thus emphasising the effects of structures situated at different levels; theoretical gravity maps of this type are known as *continuation* maps.

Increasing use is made today of digital computers to compute residual, second-derivative and continuation maps from values at grid intersections on gravity maps employing digital wavelength filters to separate shallow and deep anomalies of different wavelengths.

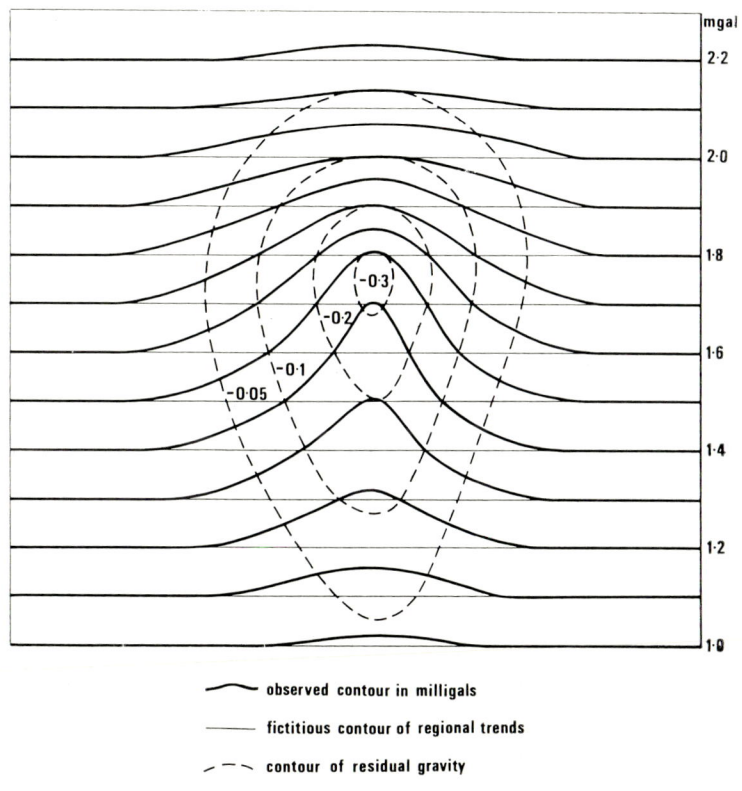

Figure 21. Residual gravity map prepared by subtracting projected regional gravity contours from actual observed contours.

(After Dobrin, *Geophysical Prospecting*, McGraw-Hill Book Co. Inc., 1960).

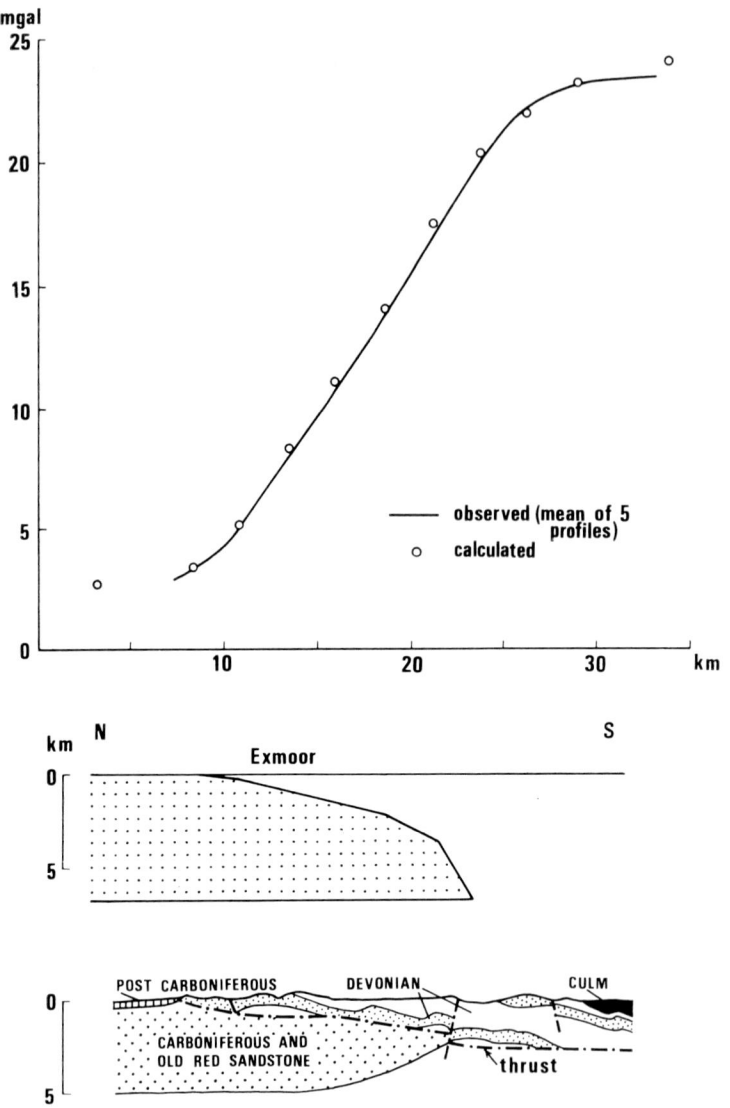

Figure 22. Observed gravity profile across West Somerset, calculated profile for hypothetical model (*centre, below profile*) and, *below*, geological section postulated to conform with hypothetical model and known geology. (After Bott & Scott, *Present views on some aspects of the geology of Cornwall and Devon*, R. Geol. Soc. Cornwall 1966)

30

Geological Interpretation

For some purposes the Bouguer Anomaly and residual gravity maps are adequate in themselves; the anomalies in the shape of gravity deficiencies, excesses and gradients which they reveal will be investigated by other methods. But these maps can be interpreted in geological terms, though such interpretations are always inherently ambiguous. Basically the method is trial-and-error comparison of the calculated gravity profiles of geological structures thought likely to exist in the area with the profile actually observed (Fig. 22).

The gravity profiles of buried masses of either greater or lesser density than the surrounding rocks have been calculated for various simple

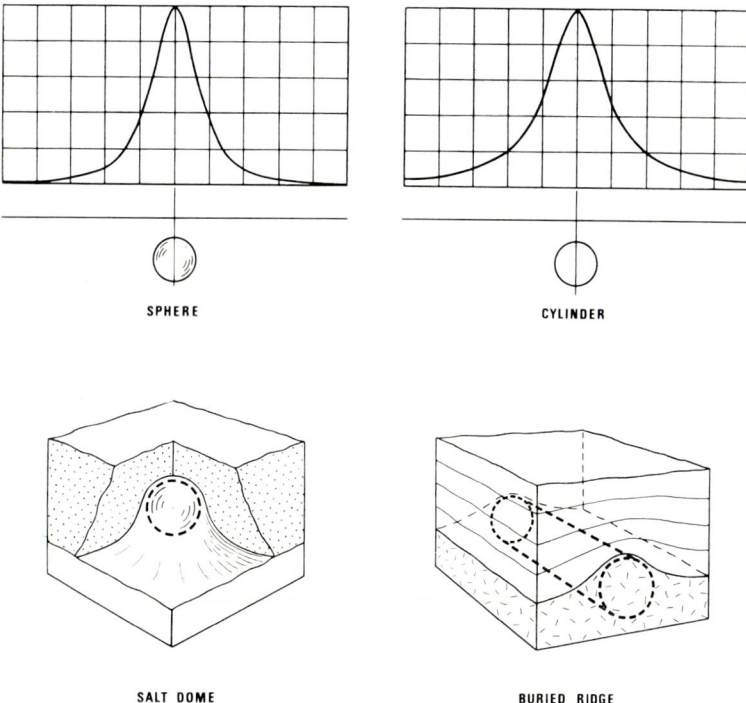

SPHERE CYLINDER

SALT DOME BURIED RIDGE

Figure 23. Geological structures such as salt domes and buried ridges may be simulated by simple geometric shapes for purposes of depth calculation. Observed profile is compared with theoretical profiles for different depths, dimensions and density contrasts.

31

geometrical shapes such as spheres, cylinders, slabs and prisms. Many geological structures approximate in form to such simple shapes; for example, a buried ridge or anticline resembles a buried horizontal cylinder and a salt dome a sphere or upright cylinder (Fig. 23). The gravity profiles of bodies of irregular shape can be computed graphically by superimposing special transparent templates or graticules over the cross-section of the body. However, two other variables apart from shape, namely the *depth* to the buried mass and its *density contrast* with the surrounding rocks enter into these calculations and affect the form of the gravity profile. The same gravity profile can be produced by many possible combinations of shape, density contrast and depth. Thus any kind of additional geological or geophysical information such as bore-hole measurements, surface structural data and seismic results, which will reduce these variables, serves to narrow the possibilities. Much of the tedious work involved in calculating gravity profiles and comparing them with observed profiles is now done with the aid of digital computers.

Magnetic Methods

Magnetic methods are mainly used in regional reconnaissance surveys, mostly airborne, and for detailed follow-up investigations of magnetic and other anomalies which might be caused by orebodies.

Basic Principles

The Earth is a huge magnet surrounded by a weak magnetic field in which the lines of force converge at the North and South Magnetic Poles. At any given moment, the Earth's magnetic field displays both world-wide and regional irregularities of direction and strength. It also undergoes progressive long-term changes with time, and is further subject to diurnal variations of strength caused by ionospheric electrical activity and to episodic disturbances or 'magnetic storms' linked with sunspot activity. Superimposed on the regional pattern of the Earth's magnetic field are local anomalies produced by variations in the intensity of magnetization of rock formations. Part of this magnetization is *induced* by the Earth's magnetic field and part is *permanent* or *natural remanent* magnetization dating from the time when the rocks were formed.

The intensity of the magnetization induced in a mineral or rock by a magnetic field of given strength is determined by its *susceptibility*, which can be measured in the laboratory or in the field. The susceptibility of some ferromagnetic minerals, in particular magnetite, is exceedingly large. The susceptibilities of rocks, which are almost entirely determined by their content of ferromagnetic minerals, chiefly magnetite, are in general much lower. Most sedimentary rocks have very low susceptibilities, whilst those of acid igneous and metamorphic rocks are fairly high and basic igneous rocks very high. However, it is increasingly realized that the induced magnetization of ferromagnetic minerals and igneous rocks, especially the more basic types, is generally much exceeded by their natural remanent magnetization.

The large local anomalies near bodies of magnetite iron ore and base metal deposits containing the magnetic mineral pyrrhotite have been known and utilized in prospecting for centuries. In modern aeromagnetic reconnaissance surveys, the geophysicist, while looking for anomalies of this type, is also concerned with the mapping and geological interpretation of the much smaller but more extensive anomalies produced by weakly magnetic rock formations.

33

Equipment and Instruments

The strength of a magnetic field is measured in *oersteds*, 1 oersted being the field strength at a distance of 1 centimetre from a magnetic pole that will repel with a force of 1 dyne a like magnetic pole at the same distance. The average strength of the Earth's magnetic field is about 0.5 oersted. The variations associated with magnetized rock formations are very much smaller than this; the practical unit in magnetic surveying is therefore the *gamma*, which is one hundred-thousandth of an oersted.

A considerable variety of magnetometers has been developed for geophysical exploration. The three types in general use in this country are the torsion-fibre, flux-gate and proton or nuclear precession magnetometers. All three are used for ground surveys, but only the flux-gate and proton magnetometers can be used in airborne and marine work. These may to some extent be supplanted in the future by the very sensitive rubidium-vapour, caesium-vapour and metastable helium magnetometers for both ground and airborne use.

Figure 24. Sharpe Instruments portable flux-gate magnetometer used to measure the vertical component of the Earth's magnetic field in magnetic traverses.
IGS photo

Figure 25. Littlemore proton magnetometer in use during a mineral survey. The water-bottle sensing element is mounted on top of a short strut in the background.

IGS photo

The *torsion-fibre magnetometer* measures changes in the vertical component of the Earth's magnetic field. The mechanism comprises a small magnetic needle fixed athwart a horizontal torsion-fibre and free to rotate about the axis of the fibre. The needle is deflected downwards from the horizontal reference position by the Earth's field. A mirror attached to the needle shows the deflection in an autocollimator telescope. The magnetometer, after levelling, is read by returning the needle to the horizontal reference position by adjusting two compensating magnets with micrometer drums. The accuracy of the instrument is about 1 gamma.

The *flux-gate magnetometer*, as adapted for ground use (Fig. 24), measures changes in the vertical component of the Earth's field; the airborne and marine versions measure changes in the total field whatever its direction. A high-permeability magnetic core is energized by an alternating current large enough nearly to saturate it. The magnetic flux in the core, as measured in a secondary coil wound on it, is augmented or opposed by the Earth's magnetic field in opposite half-cycles of the input current. When this happens, voltage pulses which are even harmonics of the input current frequency appear in the secondary coil output. The second harmonic with twice the frequency of the input current is directly proportional in amplitude to the Earth's magnetic field; it is filtered out, amplified, rectified and recorded on a continuous moving-pen recorder in the airborne and marine versions. The magnetic core or cores in these versions are kept aligned with the Earth's field by a sensing and servomotor system. The ground instrument, after levelling, gives a direct reading in gammas. The accuracy of the flux-gate magnetometer is 1 gamma.

The sensing element in the ingenious *proton magnetometer* (Fig. 25) is simply a bottle of water wound round with a coil. Protons (nuclei of hydrogen atoms) in the water, spinning about their magnetic axes, tend to align themselves with these axes

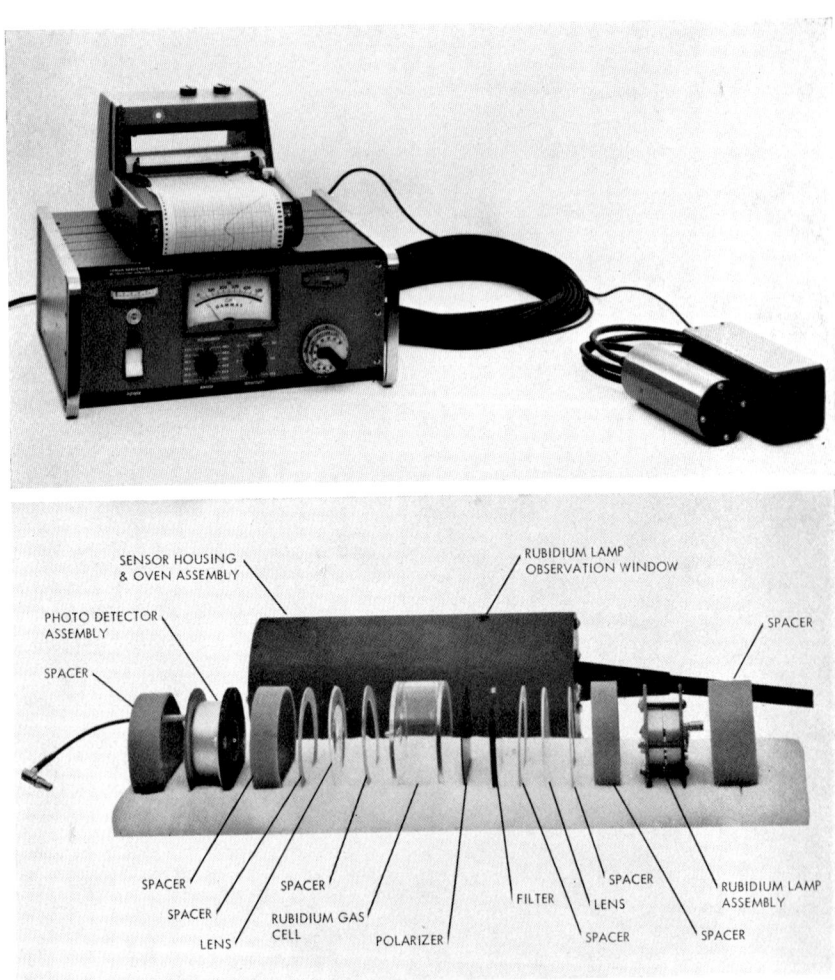

Figure 26. *Above,* Varian rubidium magnetometer: *on the left* is the readout and recording unit; *on the right*, at the end of the cable, the sensor and sensor electronics. *Below* is a view of the sensor expanded to show component parts. *Varian Associates*

parallel to the Earth's magnetic field. When a strong magnetic field at right angles to the Earth's field is applied from the coil, the protons are re-orientated in the new direction. If the applied field is now cut off suddenly, the spinning protons start to precess (revolve with their spin-axes describing a cone) around the Earth's field. The precessional oscillations induce a small voltage in the coil, the frequency of which is proportional to the strength of the Earth's magnetic field. The frequency is measured electronically and recorded digitally on punched or magnetic tape in airborne installations. In the portable ground instrument it is converted either directly to gammas or inverse gammas and read off dials. The proton magnetometer measures to an accuracy of less than 1 gamma the *absolute* value of the *total* magnetic field. It has, however, the disadvantage that, because the switching and frequency-measuring cycle takes a few seconds, the record is discontinuous. The *Sud Aviation forced-precession magnetometer* uses a very high frequency alternating magnetic field to excite the electrons in a special fluid. The electrons, through electromagnetic coupling, force the protons in the fluid to precess. The energy input is least when the protons' forced-precession frequency corresponds with their natural precession frequency in the Earth's magnetic field and resonance occurs. The frequency of the applied field at resonance will continuously fluctuate with the Earth's magnetic field, thus affording a continuous record.

The *rubidium-vapour, caesium-vapour and metastable helium magnetometers* are based on optical 'pumping' and the Zeeman effect. Electrons in the atoms of a gas follow different orbits representing higher or lower energy levels. In an external magnetic field such as the Earth's, these energy levels are split into energy sublevels or Zeeman states as the orientations of the electrons' magnetic axes differ in various degrees from, and precess around, the direction of the external magnetic field; the energy differences of the Zeeman states are proportional to the strength of the magnetic field. The rubidium magnetometer sensing element (Fig. 26) consists of a rubidium-vapour lamp, a filter to select one spectral line, a circular-polarizer, a rubidium vapour cell and a photocell. The circularly-polarized rubidium light 'pumps' electrons from *lower* Zeeman sublevels of a lower-energy orbit to Zeeman sublevels of a higher-energy orbit from which they fall back, tending to accumulate in the *highest* Zeeman sublevel of the lower-energy orbit; while this happens the cell absorbs light energy. The electrons accumulated in this highest Zeeman sublevel are returned to the *lower* Zeeman sublevels and back into the pumping cycle by stimulation from a variable frequency radio oscillator coil. The automatically varied radio frequency required to keep the cell at maximum light absorption (detected by the photocell which monitors the light and controls the radio frequency) corresponds to the natural precession frequency and is directly proportional to the energy differences of the Zeeman states and hence to the Earth's magnetic field. The accuracy of these magnetometers is as high as 0.01 gammas.

In aeromagnetic work, the magnetometer sensing element is carried in a bomb-shaped capsule or 'bird' flown on the end of a cable or is housed in a boom or 'stinger' extending back from the tail of the aircraft (Fig. 27).

Aeromagnetic Surveys and Data Processing

Aeromagnetic surveying has almost completely supplanted ground surveys for regional reconnaissance purposes. Its main advantages are speed, economy, freedom from local magnetic interference, continuity of measurement and immunity from accessibility problems. Much of the ground magnetic surveying carried out nowadays is detailed follow-up work on anomalies revealed by aeromagnetic surveys.

AEROMAGNETIC SURVEYS

Accurate identification of the plan position of the aircraft for the whole duration of the magnetometer record is essential. This is achieved *either* by taking during the flight a continuous film-strip of the flight path *or* by the use of ground-to-air radionavigation aids or airborne Doppler radar and inertial navigation systems. The film-strip is subsequently

Figure 27. Tail of Prince aeromagnetic survey aircraft showing boom or 'stinger' housing a flux-gate magnetometer.

IGS photo

38

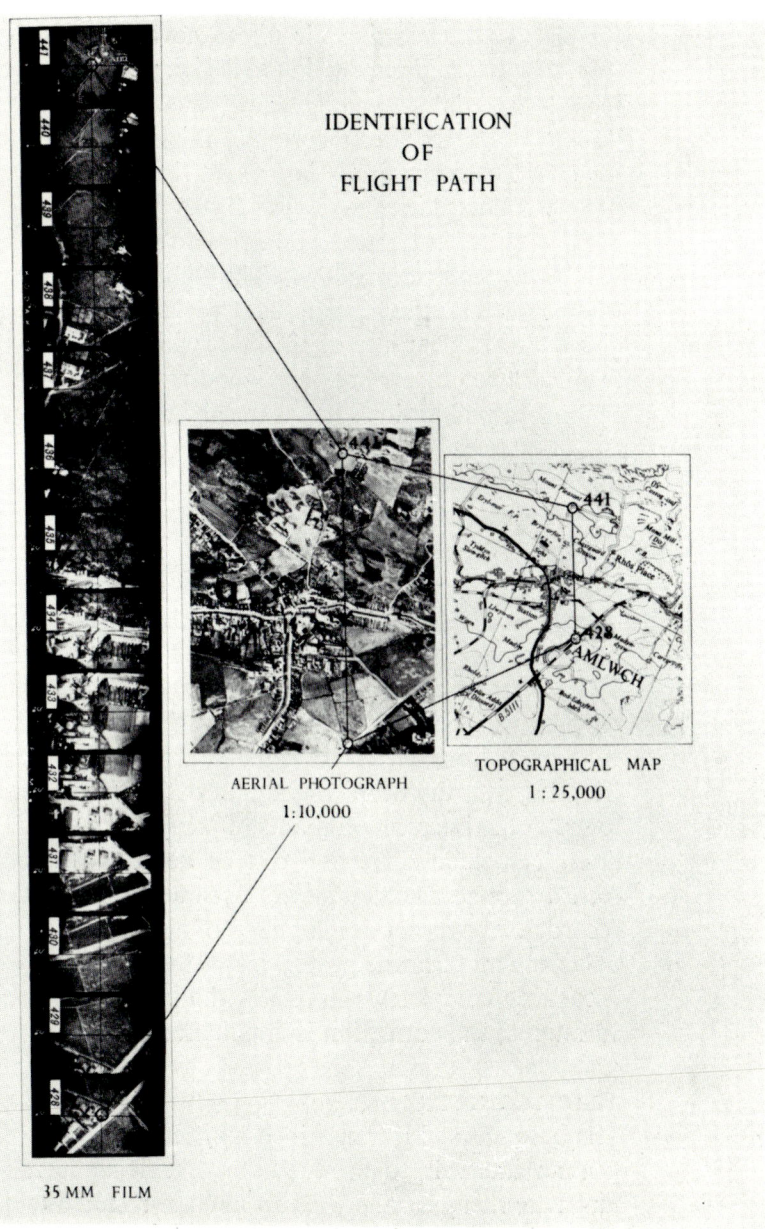

IDENTIFICATION
OF
FLIGHT PATH

AERIAL PHOTOGRAPH
1:10,000

TOPOGRAPHICAL MAP
1 : 25,000

35 MM FILM

Figure 28. Identification of the aircraft flight-path in aeromagnetic surveying by correlating film-strip taken during flight with existing air photo cover and base map of the area. *Hunting Geology and Geophysics Ltd.*

correlated with existing air photo cover and finally with base maps (Fig. 28); the radionavigation aids give position in co-ordinates and the Doppler/inertial systems give accurate speed and track data. The continuous magnetometer record and the film-strip or flight-log are keyed together by electronically impressed time or distance marks. The flight pattern followed in many regional surveys is a grid consisting of a series of parallel tracks about 1 kilometre apart crossed at 10 kilometre intervals by perpendicular tie-lines. The flight altitude depends on the terrain; where possible, the aircraft is flown at a constant altitude chosen to give a terrain clearance of 1000 feet which avoids magnetic interference from surface objects but gives good resolution of magnetic anomalies. In mineral exploration surveys the flight altitude is normally much lower.

DATA PROCESSING

After the flight lines have been identified on the base map, the magnetic strength values on the magnetometer record of all maxima, minima, change-of-slope points and positions of values corresponding to the selected contour intervals are transcribed to the base map. The values on the magnetometer record are read off from a base line or datum which incorporates corrections for the diurnal variations in the Earth's magnetic field and for the regional variation of the Earth's field computed from a formula. The diurnal correction is made by statistically distributing over the whole flight pattern the differences in magnetic values found at the intersection points of parallel tracks and perpendicular tie-lines. The same correction can be done by reference to continuous-record ground magnetometers accurately timed in with the airborne recorder. The recent development of air-to-ground telemetry of the signals from an airborne proton magnetometer via a ground proton magnetometer completely eliminates the need to correct later for diurnal variations; the correction is simultaneous and automatic.

AEROMAGNETIC MAPS

The base map with transcribed magnetic values is contoured at 5 or 10 gamma intervals to produce the aeromagnetic map. Regional aeromagnetic maps can be used to prepare residual and second-derivative magnetic maps which, like their gravity counterparts, emphasize local anomalies and outline the magnetized rock formations that cause them. In the graphical methods of preparing residual magnetic maps, the

40

Figure 29. Digital wavelength filtering: *top*, aeromagnetic map showing numerous short-wavelength anomalies due to surface volcanic rocks (left of dashed line) and longer-wavelength anomalies (right of dashed line) due to basement features; *centre*, same map filtered to reveal regional basement anomalies; *bottom*, same map filtered to emphasize residual, shallow anomalies due to volcanic rocks. (Zurflueh, *Geophysics*, 1967, Vol. 32, Soc. Explor. Geophysicists)

0   5   10

miles

41

broad, smooth regional contours associated with large-scale basement features are sketched in on an overlay and the magnetic values subtracted at intersections of the assumed regional and the actual magnetic contours. The same subtraction of regional gradients can be performed on magnetic profiles. Analytical methods using a superimposed grid, averaging values around central points and subtracting the averages from the values at the central points, can be used in conjunction with graphical methods. Second-derivative maps, which are closely related to residual maps, show the rate of change of vertical magnetic gradient. They will, if the spacing of the points on the grids used in their construction is correct, emphasize local anomalies at the expense of both broad-scale, deep-seated effects and superficial magnetic 'noise'. The preparation of residual, second-derivative and continuation maps is

Figure 30. Two rubidium magnetometers accurate to 0.01 gamma, flown at constant separation from a helicopter, are used to measure directly the vertical magnetic gradient.
Varian Associates

much simplified when a digital computer is used to make the calculations at grid points or to apply wavelength filters which separate shallow and deep anomalies of differing wavelength (Fig. 29). With the advent of the very sensitive optically-pumped magnetometers, it is now possible directly to produce vertical derivative maps showing magnetic gradients. Two magnetometers are flown a constant vertical distance apart from the same aircraft (Fig. 30). As only the differences in magnetic field at each magnetometer are being recorded, diurnal corrections are unnecessary.

Ground Magnetic Surveys

The aim of most ground surveys today is to produce accurate magnetic profiles (Fig. 31) across anomalies to enable the form and depth of the

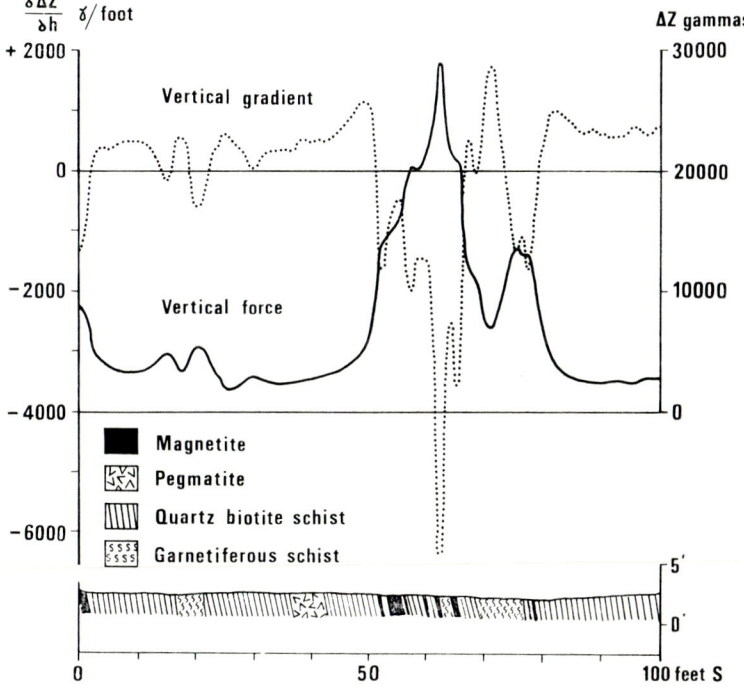

Figure 31. Profiles of vertical component of magnetic field and vertical magnetic gradient across magnetite iron ore layers near Nakina, Northern Ontario, from ground survey using portable flux-gate magnetometer.

(After Hood, *Can. Mining Jnl.*, 1964)

causative magnetized body to be computed. Portable torsion-fibre and flux-gate magnetometers measuring changes in the vertical component of the Earth's magnetic field are usually the most convenient for this work. Profiles are surveyed across the trend of linear anomalies with stations at intervals of as little as 2 feet if necessary. A base station is established beyond the anomaly where the geomagnetic field is uniform; the reading at the base station is taken as zero and all subsequent readings are expressed as plus-or-minus differences. Care must be taken to avoid iron objects and power lines, and the operator should not carry magnetic material on his person. Diurnal corrections are made either by repeat readings at the stations during the day or by running a continuous-recording magnetometer at the base station. All survey work is stopped if the latter indicates a magnetic storm in progress.

Geological Interpretation

Much information can be gained from a purely qualitative assessment of aeromagnetic and ground magnetic maps in conjunction with other geological and geophysical data. Magnetic maps of areas in which igneous rocks and ore deposits are concentrated at or near the surface show numerous closely spaced anomalies with steep gradients. Basins filled with thick sequences of virtually non-magnetic sedimentary rock show up as areas of widely spaced contours. Sharply defined anomalies transgressive to regional trends may occur over magnetic igneous intrusions in magnetically 'inactive' sedimentary sequences (Fig. 32). Where a magnetically 'active' basement is present at shallow depths under sedimentary cover, the magnetic map may show a variety of anomalies including linear gradients caused by fractures on one side of which the basement is nearer the surface, enclosed 'highs' produced by highly magnetized rocks in the basement and local linear or enclosed anomalies caused by uplifts or buried ridges and hills on the basement surface. None of these features, with which might be associated oil, gas or mineral deposits, may be evident from geological maps.

From ground survey profiles and airborne magnetometer records it is possible to study anomalies and make calculations of the depths to magnetized rocks beneath them. These calculations involve assumptions as to the form of the magnetized body and its degree of magnetization. The calculated magnetic profiles of buried magnetized bodies of various shapes are compared with the actual profile. The method is very similar to that used in gravity interpretations and has the same limitations of ambiguity. An additional complication is that the profile shape is influenced by the direction of magnetization of the body as well as its size, shape, depth and degree of magnetization. Owing to natural remanent magnetization, this direction may not correspond to the present-day Earth's field. The digital computer promises to help greatly in the lengthy calculations involved in matching theoretical magnetic profiles with observed profiles.

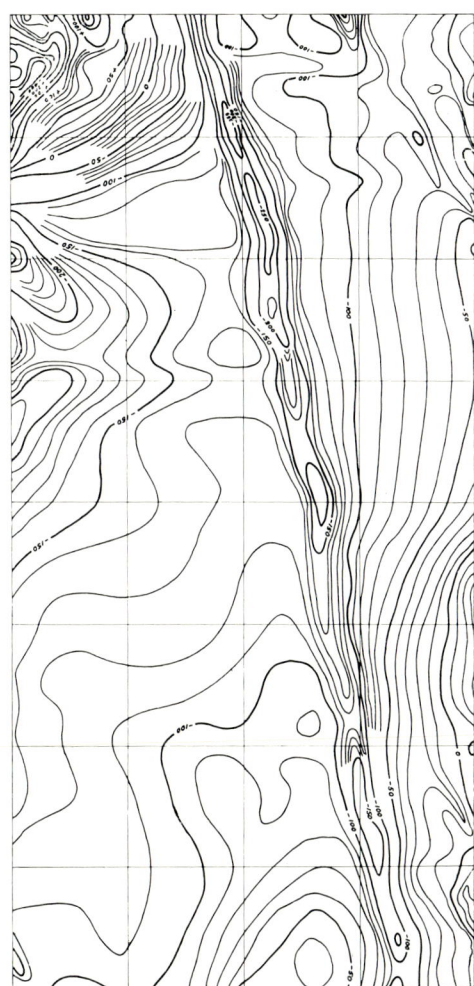

Figure 32. Aeromagnetic map showing sharp linear anomaly probably due to strongly magnetized Tertiary basalt dyke in weakly magnetized sedimentary rocks north of Isle of Skye.

Electrical and Electromagnetic Methods

These methods are used almost exclusively in prospecting for ore deposits and in site investigation for engineering projects; their depth of penetration is normally too shallow for oil and gas exploration. They may be divided into those in which natural electrical and electromagnetic fields in the Earth are measured and those that measure the effects of artificially applied fields.

Methods Using Natural Fields

SELF-POTENTIAL (SP) METHOD

Small electrical currents generated by local electrochemical action will flow between two non-polarizing electrodes placed a short distance apart anywhere in the ground. While normally of the order of a few millivolts, the potentials associated with these currents may reach values of several hundred millivolts in the vicinity of metallic sulphide orebodies and graphite deposits.

Promising areas are tested by placing two electrodes on the ground a constant distance apart along staked-out lines and recording the potential gradients at regular intervals along them. A self-potential profile (Fig. 33) will, if there is no undue interference from irregularities of terrain, show a pronounced dip over the orebody.

TELLURIC METHOD

This is the only electrical method that has been successfully applied to the search for oil and gas; it played a major part in the discovery of the great Lacq oil and gas field in south-western France.

Telluric currents are fluctuating and oscillating small currents which flow in vast sheets involving the entire surface of the Earth. They are induced in conductive rocks by the magneto-telluric field, an oscillating natural electromagnetic field responsible for the diurnal variations in the Earth's magnetic field and caused by ionospheric electrical activity. Like the Earth's magnetic field, they show large diurnal and geographical variations of intensity and direction.

The flow pattern and current density of telluric currents is affected by resistivity variations in rock formations; it is thus possible to map out areas of relatively high resistivity where resistant formations approach the surface. Arched strata also tend to show up as resistant areas, since telluric currents have to penetrate the stratification in traversing such uplifts.

Simultaneous photographic records are taken of the potentials or electric field strengths in the north and east direction measured between pairs of electrodes at a base station and at field stations several miles or tens of miles apart. The ratio of the average potential gradient at the field station to that of the base station is plotted for each field station and all values are contoured (Fig. 34). The vectors of the electrical field are also measured; they indicate lateral gradients and discontinuities in rock conductance. Electrified railways and similar sources of earth current must be avoided.

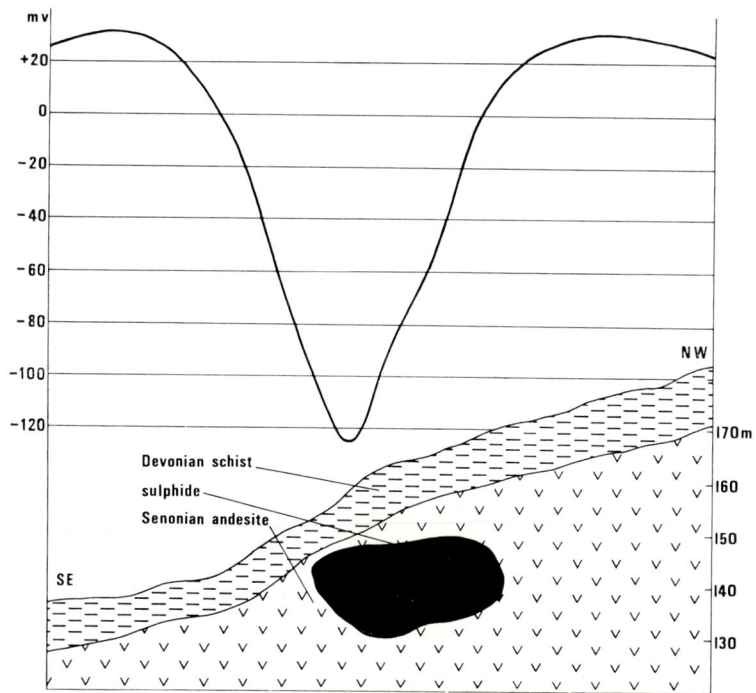

Figure 33. Self-potential profile over sulphide orebody, Sariyer, Turkey.

(After Yüngül, *Geophysics*, 1954)

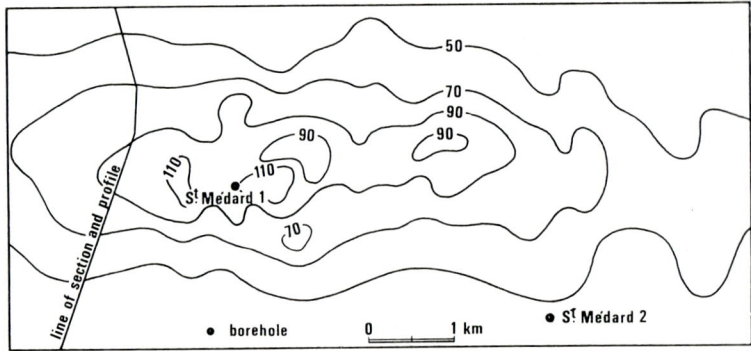

Telluric map of St. Médard anticline

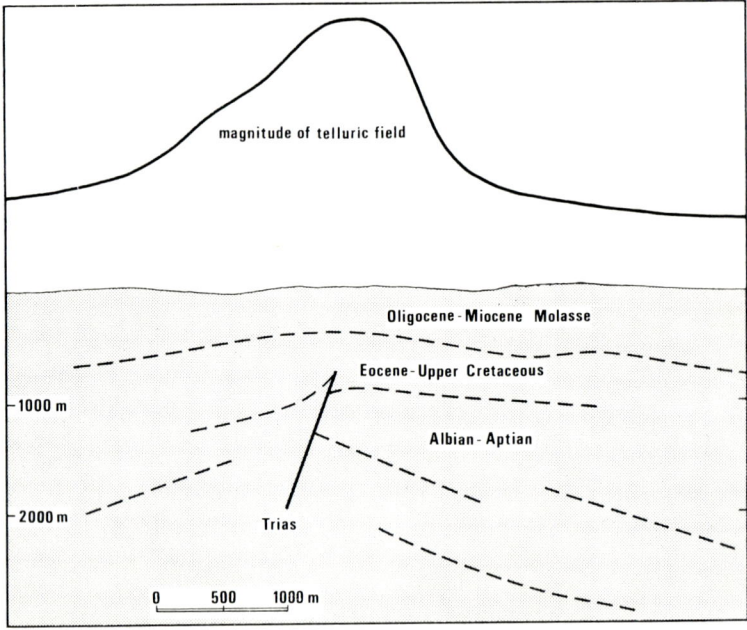

Seismic and telluric cross-section

Figure 34. *Above:* Telluric map of the St. Médard anticline, Pyrenean foothills, showing contours of equal magnitude of the telluric field. *Below:* telluric profile and seismic section across the St. Médard anticline. (After Beaufort and others, *Geophysical Case Histories*, Vol. 2, Soc. Explor. Geophysicists, 1956)

In the closely related magneto-telluric method, the horizontal component of the magneto-telluric field is measured simultaneously with measurement of the telluric currents. From these measurements, estimates can be made of the absolute resistivity and thickness of crustal rocks to very great depths.

AFMAG METHOD

The name AFMAG derives from the alternating Audio-Frequency MAGnetic fields utilized in this method. These are pulses of natural electromagnetic waves, supposedly caused by world-wide thunderstorm activity, which are propagated in the natural waveguide formed by the ionosphere and the Earth's surface. The direction of propagation is normally in a strictly horizontal plane but in a variable and rather vague direction in azimuth. In the vicinity of conductive material, such as a massive sulphide orebody, the waves dip down from the horizontal and assume a more definite direction in azimuth.

The method is well adapted to airborne use. The detection system consists of two search coils 90° to each other, sharing a common horizontal diameter with the plane of each coil 45° to the horizontal, housed in a 'bird' towed at the end of a cable from an aircraft flying at an altitude of around 500 feet. Dips in the wave propagation direction are registered as unequal induced voltages in the coils. These are recorded on a continuous paper record to give AFMAG profiles (Fig. 35) from which the location and size of the orebody can be deduced. A photographic film-strip of the flight path, necessary for position location, also enables interfering electric power lines to be identified.

In ground use, to measure the dip angle, the coils are rotated about their common horizontal diameter to a position of minimum signal noise and the inclination of the plane of the upright coil noted. The azimuth direction is ascertained by turning the coils in the direction of maximum signal noise. Measurements are made at intervals of 100 to 200 feet along traverses perpendicular to the assumed geological strike. Dip readings plotted as longer or shorter arrows locate the conductive orebody.

The AFMAG method is more effective in locating mineralized or potentially mineralized conductive zones rather than small, highly conductive orebodies.

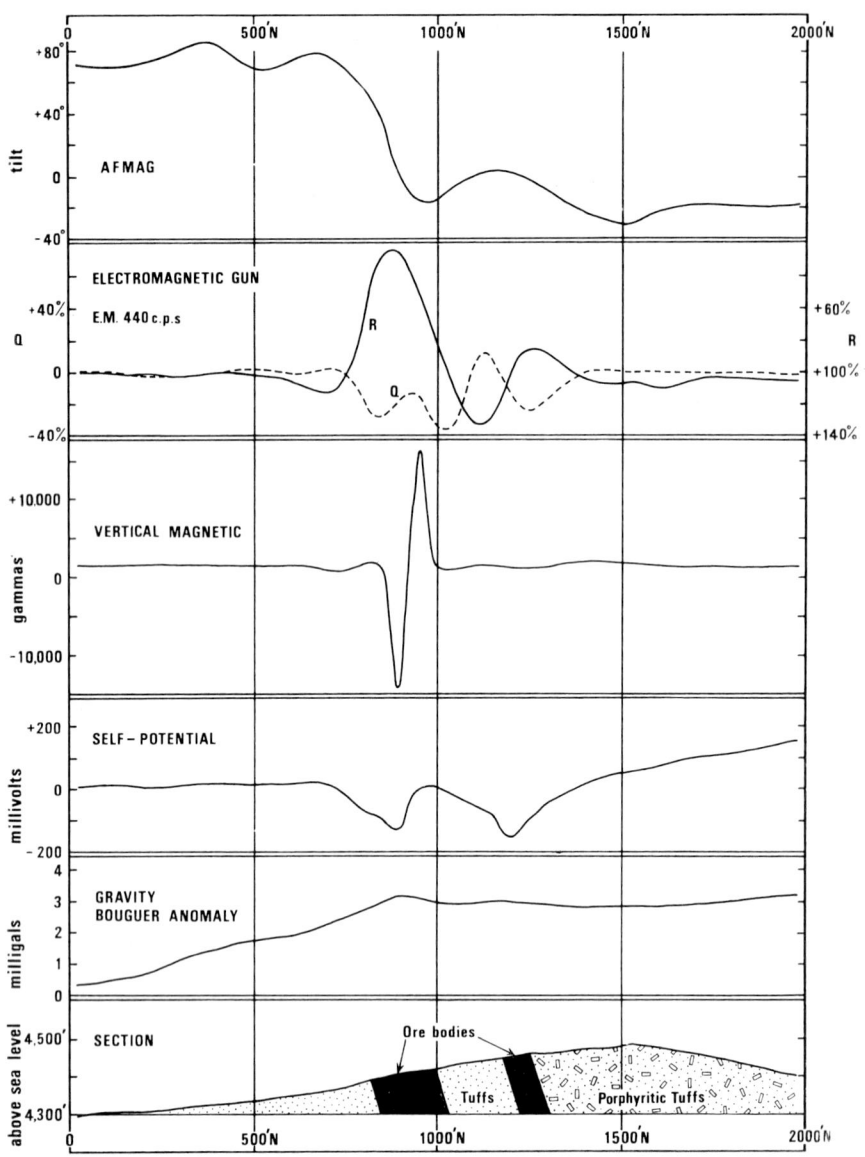

Figure 35. Ground AFMAG profile over the Samena sulphide orebody, Geita, Tanzania (*top*) compared with profiles by other geophysical methods.
(After Makowiecki, King & Cratchley, *IGS Geophy. Pap. No.* 3, 1969)

Methods Using Artificially Applied Fields

EQUIPOTENTIAL-LINE METHOD

This is the simplest of the methods employing artificial currents. A voltage applied to two electrodes inserted in the ground will cause a current to flow through the ground between them. In uniformly conductive ground, the lines of current flow follow a regular pattern similar to the lines of force around a bar magnet (Fig. 36). The current flow-lines trend everywhere perpendicular to so-called equipotential lines along

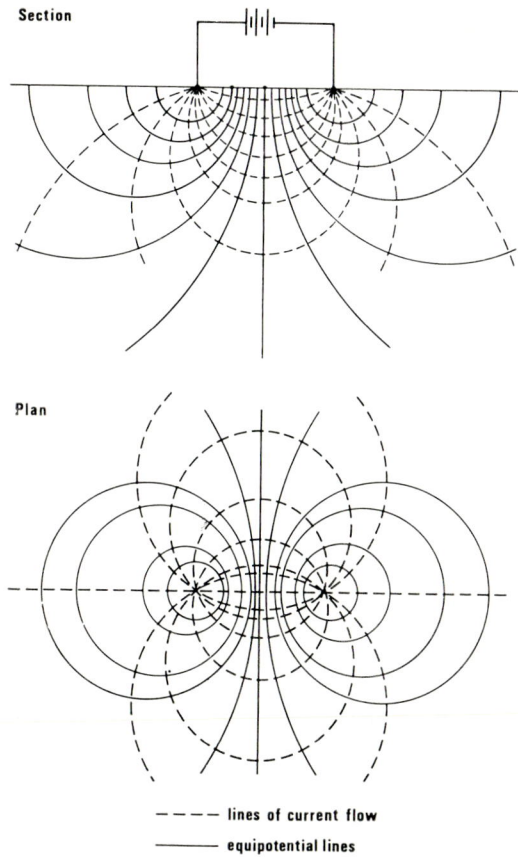

---- lines of current flow

———— equipotential lines

Figure 36. Lines of current flow and equipotential lines in uniformly conductive ground. (After Dobrin, *Geophysical Prospecting*, McGraw-Hill Book Co. Inc., 1960)

51

which the voltages are equal. If, however, a body of material having a different conductivity to its surroundings is interposed in the current flow, the lines of flow are distorted, either away from the body if its conductivity is lower or towards it if higher (Fig. 37); the equipotential lines will also be distorted. Highly conductive orebodies can thus be located. It is not possible directly to map current flow-lines, but the equipotential lines can be located. The earth is energized from a pair of primary electrodes about 2000 feet apart, across which a portable generator maintains a voltage of about 200 volts. The equipotential lines are mapped with the aid of two search electrodes, one of which is fixed between the primary electrodes while the other is used to locate points where the voltage difference between the two search electrodes is nil.

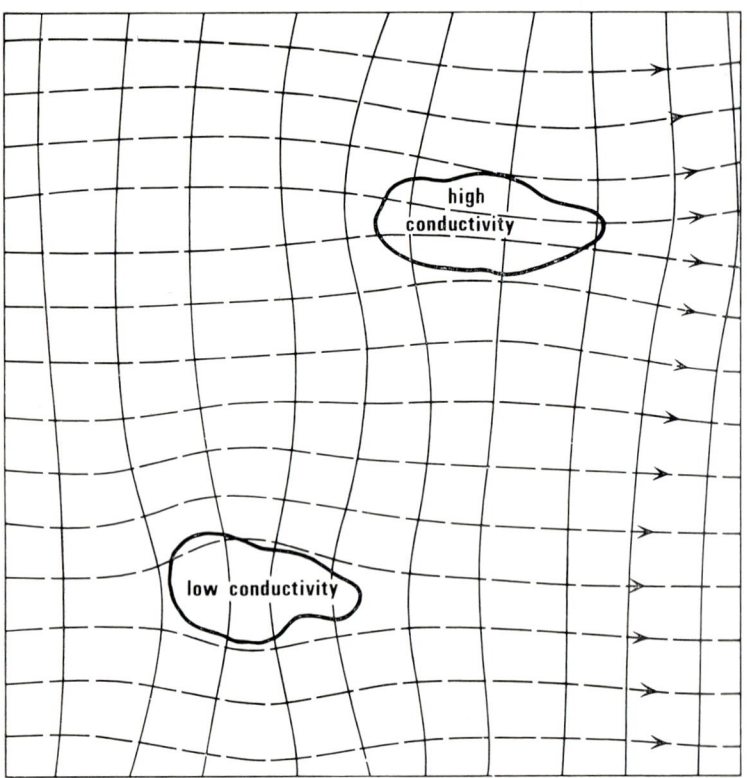

Figure 37. Distortion of current flow and equipotential lines by bodies of contrasting conductivity.

These methods have been widely used in determining the shape and depth of orebodies, the depth to bedrock in engineering projects and in groundwater studies. They are basically similar to the equipotential-line method in that a current is passed through the ground between electrodes, but it is the potential *gradients* in between that are measured rather than lines of nil gradient. Irregularities in the conductivity of rocks in the ground affect the relation between the current applied to the current electrodes and the voltage drop measured between the potential electrodes. These irregularities can be interpreted in terms of depths to layers (such as bedrock surfaces) or orebodies with anomalously high or low resistivities.

The field procedure involves laying out the current and potential electrodes along staked lines (Fig. 38). Several different methods of spacing the electrodes are employed; in most of these the potential electrodes are placed between the current electrodes. In the *Wenner*

Figure 38. Resistivity survey using ABEM Terrameter equipment. The electrodes in the foreground are spaced in the Wenner arrangement.   *IGS photo*

arrangement (Fig. 39), the electrode spacings are equal; the spacings can be progressively increased, keeping the centre of the array fixed *or* the whole array with fixed spacing can be shifted from place to place along a staked line. In the *Schlumberger* arrangement (Fig. 39), the potential electrodes with a small constant separation are shifted between fixed current electrodes, or the latter may be moved apart between readings on the constant-separation potential electrodes. Another method is to use two parallel bare wires laid out on the ground 1000 yards apart as current electrodes and to move the pair of potential electrodes along parallel lines perpendicular to the current wires.

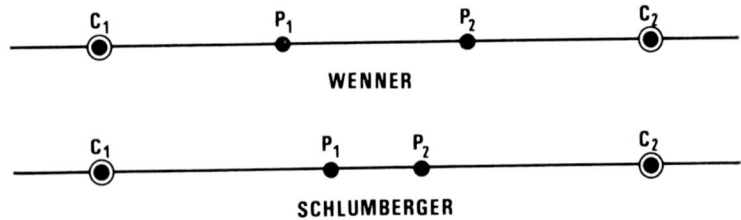

Figure 39. *Wenner* and *Schlumberger* electrode arrangements.

For each position of the array in the Wenner arrangement, an apparent resistivity of the ground is calculated and plotted on a map at the mid-point of the array; the values are then contoured. Orebodies show up as resistivity anomalies. Measurements taken with the centre of the array fixed and with the electrodes separated by progressively larger distances can be used to calculate depths to horizontal resistivity discontinuities such as bedrock surface beneath soil overburden. Depth estimation is facilitated by comparing the actual apparent-resistivity profiles with theoretical computer-calculated curves for superposed layers of different thicknesses and resistivities. A particularly useful method for estimating the size of orebodies which have been located by a few drill holes is to insert the electrodes down the drill-holes into the orebody, subsequently using special curves to arrive at the shape of the orebody.

INDUCED POLARIZATION (IP) METHOD
When an electric current passing through the ground is suddenly cut off, a small current, initially at a fraction of the original voltage and decaying

54

gradually, continues to flow for a short period of time. The phenomenon is known as *induced polarization* or *overvoltage*, and is an electrochemical effect which arises at the surfaces of buried metallic sulphide orebodies. The much-used IP method (Fig. 40) is particularly proficient in finding disseminated ore in which the ore minerals are scattered through barren rock.

Two techniques are used: 'pulse-transient or *time-domain* IP' and 'variable frequency or *frequency-domain* IP'. In the first, controlled pulses of direct current from a motor generator are passed into the ground through two current electrodes. The overvoltage between pulses is measured across two potential electrodes. In one commonly used electrode configuration, the 'three-electrode arrangement' (Fig. 41), one current electrode is fixed while the other current electrode and the two potential electrodes, all equally spaced, are moved along the traverse

Figure 40. Induced polarization survey using Huntec time-domain equipment. Motor generator in background supplies current to pulse transmitter (with operator, centre left) energizing electrodes at far left and far right. Receiver (with operator, foreground) is connected to porous-pot potential electrodes to left and right of receiver operator. *IGS photo*

55

line. The induced polarization effect is expressed as the ratio of over-voltage, integrated over a specific time interval, to the applied voltage. The 'frequency-domain' technique utilizes the observation that, when an alternating current is passed through the ground, the apparent resistivity of materials in which polarization can be induced is higher with low-frequency current than with higher-frequency current. Alternating current at two frequencies differing by a factor of ten, say 0.1 and 1 cycle per second, is fed from a generator-powered transmitter into current electrodes A and B and the apparent resistivity measured between two potential electrodes M and N in the so-called 'dipole-dipole' arrangement (Fig. 41). By moving the array at fixed electrode separations along traverses, lateral IP variations can be detected. By increasing the distance BM between current and potential electrodes in multiples of AB or MN, greater depth penetration can be obtained. The induced polarization is expressed as 'apparent metal factor', a quantity calculated from the apparent resistivities by a standard formula, which can be plotted and contoured on maps and sections (Fig. 42).

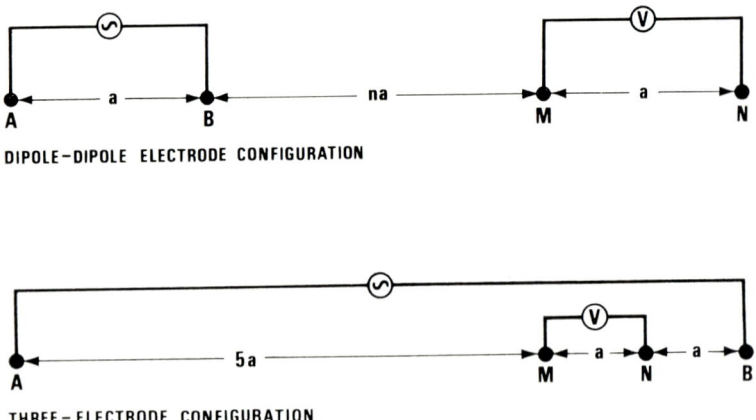

DIPOLE–DIPOLE ELECTRODE CONFIGURATION

THREE–ELECTRODE CONFIGURATION

Figure 41. Dipole-dipole and three-electrode configurations.

ELECTROMAGNETIC (EM) METHODS

Electromagnetic waves—an alternating magnetic field—produced by an alternating current flowing in a wire loop or in a wire grounded at both ends will induce alternating currents flowing in closed loops in subsur-

56

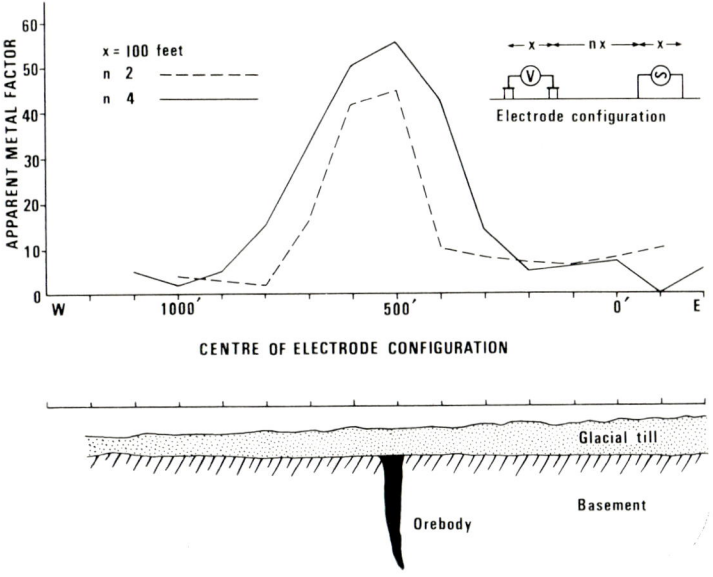

Figure 42. Induced polarization profile over vertical sulphide orebody.
(After Hallof, *Trans. Am. Inst. Engrs*, 1960)

face conductive materials such as metallic sulphide orebodies. These induced currents themselves generate secondary electromagnetic waves which distort the primary electromagnetic field. The secondary field differs in phase from the primary field and with very good conductors is almost opposite in phase; its direction also tends to differ. The resultant (primary distorted by secondary) field can thus be separated into in-phase and out-of-phase horizontal and vertical components. Electromagnetic methods measure by means of search coils, vertical or horizontal, the amplitudes and phase differences of these components or the direction of the resultant field.

Electromagnetic methods in common use today fall into two classes: those employing a *stationary* source and those employing a *mobile* source.

The stationary source is usually a single straight cable grounded at each end or a rectangular loop up to 3 miles in length, laid out parallel to the trend of the ore-zone, and energized by an alternating current from a rotary generator or oscillator-amplifier. In the *Sundberg* method, a single receiving coil and ratiometer are moved along traverses at right angles to the source cable, measuring the in-phase and out-of-phase horizontal or vertical components. The amplitudes in the receiving coil are related to the field measured in a reference coil placed near the source cable and transmitted by radio link to the ratiometer. In the closely related *Turam* method, the ratios of the in-phase and out-of-phase components of the vertical field are measured in two horizontal receiving coils and a ratiometer; the coils are kept a fixed distance of about 25 yards apart. The ratios are adjusted by a factor which, in the absence of conductors, equates them to unity. Maximum values of the amplitude ratio and minimum values of the phase difference occur over narrow vertical conductors.

The mobile source in horizontal loop methods such as *Slingram* and *EM Gun* is a horizontal coil or ferrite rod energized by a battery-operated transmitter which feeds a reference voltage through a cable to the ratiometer and a horizontal receiver coil. The source coil and receiver coil are maintained a constant distance apart, ranging from 25 to 100 yards, in an in-line traverse. The in-phase and out-of-phase components are measured as percentages of the reference voltage, the equipment having been adjusted to read 100 per cent for the in-phase and 0 per cent for the out-of-phase components in electrically neutral ground. Profiles are plotted with the values placed at the mid-point between the coils and are compared with model or theoretical curves to determine the shape and depth of the orebody. In the *dip-angle* method, which measures the direction of the resultant field, the mobile source is a vertical loop operating on either one or two frequencies. The source loop and the receiver loop (Fig. 43) are advanced at constant separation either in-line along a single traverse 45° to the regional strike or broadside along parallel traverses perpendicular to the strike. The receiver coil is then rotated in the plane of the source loop about a horizontal axis until a minimum signal is heard in the headphones. The dip-angles are read at suitable intervals off a clinometer attached to the receiver coil and are plotted on a profile to be compared with theoretical profiles.

The electromagnetic method using a mobile transmitter is readily adaptable to airborne use. Vertical transmitter and receiver loops operating on a single frequency are either mounted on the extremities of the aircraft, coplanar in the wingtips or coaxial in the nose and tail, or a

Figure 43. Electromagnetic surveying using McPhar dip-angle equipment. Receiver coil with clinometer (*above*) measures direction of resultant electromagnetic field induced by transmitter coil (*left*, in the tube).

McPhar Geophysics Ltd.

Figure 44. Prince aircraft equipped with horizontal and vertical transmitter coils for airborne electromagnetic survey by the rotary method. Receiver coils are carried in a similar aircraft. *Hunting Geology and Geophysics Ltd.*

dual-frequency horizontal transmitter loop is slung between wingtips and tail, the vertical receiver loop being flown behind and below in a 'bird'. In the rotating-field method, the rotating field is transmitted from vertical and horizontal loops mounted on the rear fuselage co-planar with the fin and tailplane (Fig. 44). The transmitter loops are separately energized by two currents 90° out of phase with each other. The receiver loops, flown in a 'bird' or a separate aircraft, are similarly orientated with their common intersection line directed at the source so that both sets of loops are approximately coplanar. Where two air-craft are used the transmitter aircraft flies directly behind the 'bird' towed by the receiver aircraft. The amplitude of the voltage difference in the receiver coils and the phase shift measured in relation to the primary field are continuously recorded. In all airborne EM work, accurate altitude and flight-path identification are necessary.

INPUT METHOD

In this relatively new airborne method, named from the initials of the effect utilized—INduced PUlse-Transient, powerful electromagnetic pulses are transmitted from a loop antenna on the aircraft. These prim-

60

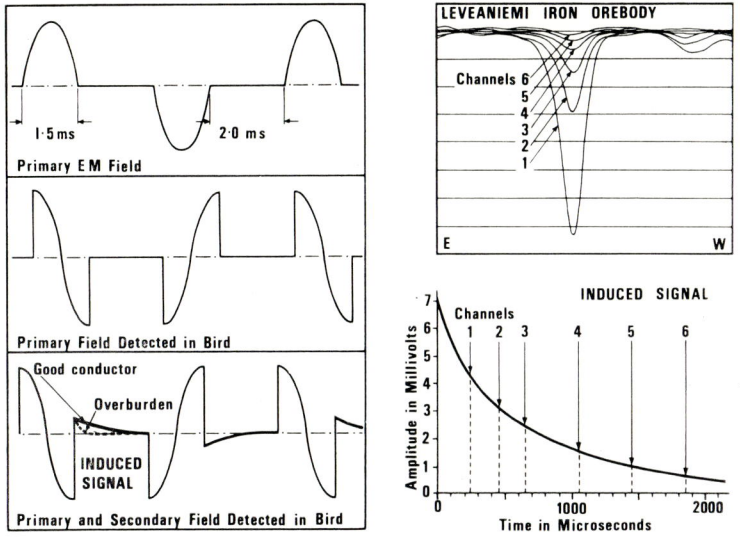

Figure 45. Waveform of transmitted and received INPUT signal with, *bottom right*, amplitude/time plot of induced transient signal showing six sampling channels and, *top right*, six-channel INPUT profile over the Leveaniemi magnetite orebody, Sweden. (After Boniwell, *Canadian Min. Met. Bull.*, 1967).

ary field pulses, each lasting for 1.5 milliseconds and separated by intervals of 2 milliseconds, induce secondary eddy currents in conductive materials in the ground. These eddy currents generate a secondary electromagnetic field which is detected by a coil in a 'bird' towed below and behind the aircraft. In the interval between pulses, the secondary field decays in a characteristic fashion: that produced by conductive overburden, such as swampland, decays very rapidly to zero long before the next primary pulse, whereas that from metallic sulphide ore takes the full interval between pulses to decay (Fig. 45). The voltage generated in the detector coil is sampled by the INPUT receiver at six fixed intervals between each primary pulse. The receiver converts the six sample voltages into coherent integrated output voltages which are recorded on a moving chart. Other apparatus in the aircraft records the total magnetic field, gamma radiation, the altitude and the aircraft position. A still newer airborne method developed by Dr. A. R. Barringer, inventor of the INPUT method, measures the field components induced by long-wave radio signals broadcast to submerged nuclear submarines.

61

Radiometric Methods

Radiometric methods are used mainly in the search for uranium and the rare 'new technology' metals with which uranium and thorium are associated in nature.

Basic Principles

Some naturally occurring isotopes, that is, varieties of an element whose atomic nuclei contain different numbers of protons and neutrons, are unstable; their atomic nuclei disintegrate spontaneously at steady rates, giving off alpha particles (helium nuclei), beta particles (electrons) or gamma rays (electromagnetic waves similar to but more energetic than X-rays). Alpha particles can penetrate only a few inches in air. Beta particles are about a hundred times more penetrating than alpha particles, and gamma rays are highly penetrating, the hardest, most energetic types passing through several hundred feet of air. The gamma radiation emitted by a gamma-active isotope covers a range or spectrum of frequencies and intensities with strong emission at certain characteristic frequencies which constitute lines in the spectrum of the element.

Most natural radioactivity strong enough to be detected by field and airborne instruments is associated with *uranium* and its radioactive decay products, *thorium* and its decay products and the transformation with gamma emission of the ^{40}K isotope of *potassium* into argon 40 by electron-capture and calcium 40 by beta-emission. Because of the low penetrating powers of alpha and beta particles, most of the radiation measured in radiometric prospecting is gamma radiation.

Instruments

The familiar *Geiger counter* used in general reconnaissance prospecting consists of a cylindrical metal cathode with a wire anode along its axis, the whole enclosed in a thin-walled tube filled with low-pressure inert gas. In operation, the cathode carries a charge of about 1000 volts, just short of that needed to produce an electrical discharge across the cathode-anode space. A charged particle or gamma ray traversing this space produces by collision with the inert gas atoms positive ions and negative electrons. Under the high voltage these are rapidly accelerated towards the cathode and anode, colliding on the way with other gas atoms and producing in a chain reaction many more charged particles. This avalanche arriving at the anode and cathode is registered as a pulse which is amplified to produce a click in a headphone set, or a succession of such pulses can be expressed as a meter reading in milliröntgens per hour or as counts per second.

But for accurate surveys, particularly from the air, more sensitive instruments than the Geiger counter are required. The *scintillation counter*, which measures gamma radiation, has been extensively used in airborne and ground radiometric surveys. It utilizes the flash of light emitted when the atoms of a suitable 'phosphor' such as a large sodium iodide crystal 'doped' with thallium are energized by gamma rays. The scintillations are detected by the light-sensitive cathode of a photomultiplier tube. The scintillations are converted by the succession of electrodes in the tube into a stream of electrons which are collected and recorded on a meter.

A development of the scintillation counter for portable and airborne use is the gamma-ray spectrometer (Fig. 46) which analyses the complex gamma-ray spectrum of uranium, thorium and potassium and indicates the relative gamma-ray contribution of each element to ground gamma-ray emission on a continuous readout.

Field and Airborne Surveys

FIELD SURVEYS

These may be 'spot' examinations of outcrops with a Geiger counter or systematic surveys on a predetermined grid, with a scintillation counter supported at a fixed height above the ground, the readings from which are plotted and contoured on a map. Only those readings 3-4 times the level of background radiation from cosmic and non-economic ground sources can be considered significant.

AIRBORNE SURVEYS

These employ sensitive scintillation counters and gamma-ray spectrometers. The flight altitude and flight-line spacing depend on the type of

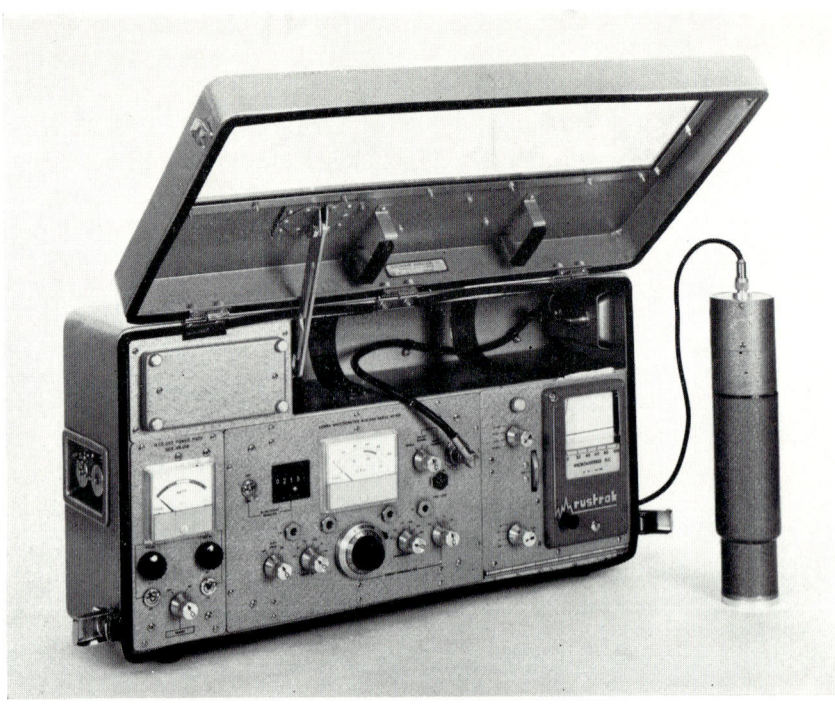

Figure 46. E.A.L. portable gamma-ray spectrometer. The tube on the right contains the sodium iodide scintillator crystal. *IGS photo*

survey and the sensitivity of the instrument. For effective ground cover, the line spacing should not exceed twice the flight altitude which is commonly about 500 feet above ground. A radio-altimeter trace is required to correct for terrain irregularities which bring the radiation source nearer the aircraft. Navigation is from air photographs or maps and the flight path is filmed for position location. Promising anomalies are followed up by ground surveys. It is common practice now to fly radiometric, magnetic and electromagnetic surveys from the same aircraft.

Borehole Logging

Geophysical measurements made by lowering specially encased miniaturized instruments into boreholes afford valuable supplementary data in geological and geophysical studies.

Seismic Measurements

The purpose of seismic or continuous velocity logging of boreholes is to obtain values of seismic speeds in formations traversed by the borehole for use in seismic reflection work. The probe lowered into the borehole utilizes a powerful electric spark to produce an acoustic pulse which is detected after passing through the wallrock by detectors spaced a few feet apart in the probe. The velocity is indicated on a continuous record or continuous velocity log (Fig. 47), from which a 'total-time' curve showing the reflection time to various depths is computed. Velocities can also be obtained by lowering a geophone into the hole and firing a shot at the surface.

Gravity Measurements

Several gravity meters have been developed for use in boreholes. The most accurate to date, made by LaCoste and Romberg, Inc. (Fig. 48), is based on their well known geodetic 'zero-length' spring gravity meter and has an accuracy of 0.015 milligal. In addition to measuring the vertical gravity gradient and rock densities and porosities, it has been used in attempting directly to locate oil accumulations which, possessing a lower density than water, give rise to small negative anomalies.

Magnetic Measurements

Measurements of both the total magnetic field, using a flux-gate or proton magnetometer, and the magnetic susceptibility of the wallrock are carried out in boreholes. These measurements are mostly made in connexion with iron-ore prospecting.

Electrical Measurement

Resistivity measurement or 'electrical logging' is a routine operation in all uncased boreholes nowadays. Such measurements are of great

65

practical importance in formation correlation from one borehole to another and in evaluating physical properties of formations, such as porosity and permeability.

Various methods are used to measure the apparent or the true resistivity. In the older, semi-quantitative single-electrode method, a simple

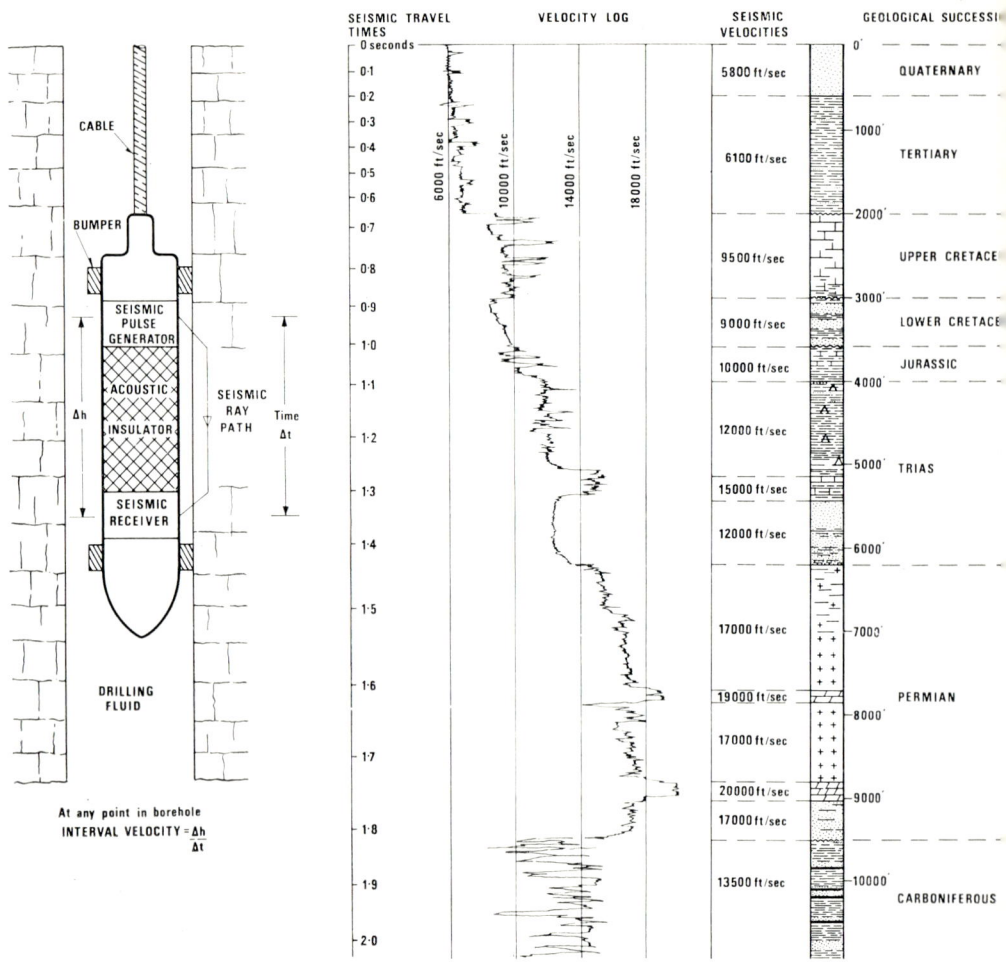

Figure 47. Seismic velocity measurement in boreholes: *left*, acoustic pulse generator; *right*, continuous velocity log and geological sequence with measured velocities.

British Petroleum Ltd.

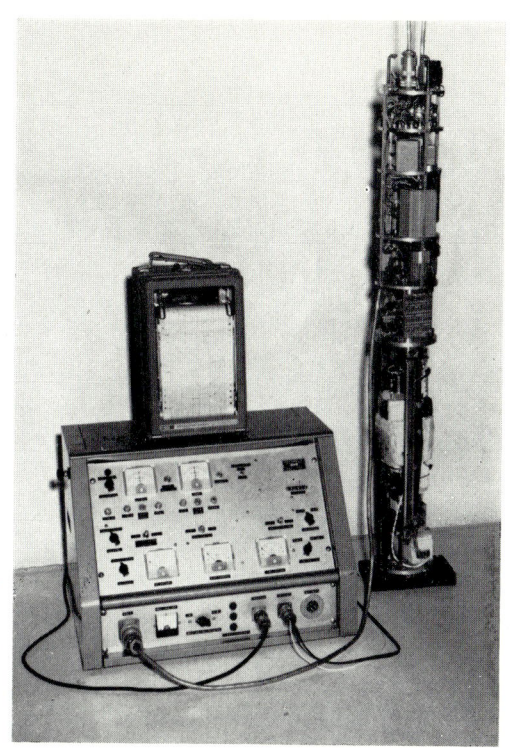

Figure 48. LaCoste and Romberg borehole gravity meter: *on the left*, recording unit with chart recorder; *on the right*, the probe incorporating the meter and measuring electronics.
  LaCoste and Romberg Inc.

circuit comprising a single downhole electrode, the water or drilling mud in the hole, the wallrock and a grounded electrode at the surface measures the resistance or apparent resistivity of the rock around the downhole electrode. A modern refinement is the focussed-current method in which the current is focussed into a disc-shaped zone by two 'guard' electrodes placed above and below the downhole current electrode and maintained at the same potential, enabling the true resistivity of the formation to be calculated. True resistivities may also be obtained in multi-electrode systems in which the potential is measured between two downhole electrodes, both grounded at the surface, one making a current circuit and the other the measuring circuit; alternatively, using the same current circuit with downhole current electrode, the potential gradient between two downhole potential electrodes can be measured.

Self-potential, induced polarization and electromagnetic induction measurements may also be carried out in boreholes. Electromagnetic induction can be used to measure resistivities in dry holes.

67

Radiometric Measurements

Continuous gamma-ray logging of boreholes with a scintillation counter is, like electrical logging, almost a routine operation following the drilling of a borehole (Fig. 49). Different rock formations possess different natural radioactivities, shales in particular displaying high radioactivity. The gamma-ray log, like the electrical log, is especially valuable in formation correlation. Density determinations in connexion with gravity surveys are carried out in boreholes by gamma-gamma logging in which a strong radioisotope gamma-source on the probe lowered into the hole irradiates the wallrock. The back-scatter gamma radiation, which is proportional to the density of the wallrock, is measured with a scintillation counter located a short distance above the source.

An artificial neutron source is used in neutron-neutron and neutron-gamma logging to detect the presence of hydrogenous substances such as oil, gas or water. Hydrogen nuclei capture neutrons and in so doing emit gamma rays (measured by a scintillation counter) and reduce the neutron flux (measured in a Geiger tube filled with boron trifluoride gas). In cased (steel-lined) boreholes, only gamma and neutron logging are possible.

Figure 49. Gamma-ray logging: probe carrying scintillation counter about to be lowered into the borehole. *IGS photo*

For the Future

Developments in geophysical exploration fall into three categories:
1. New methods utilizing geophysical effects hitherto unknown or unexploited
2. More sensitive and versatile instruments for established methods
3. Computer processing of geophysical results.

Both new methods and new instruments exploit the 'new technology' electronics. The optically-pumped gas magnetometers have opened new fields in magnetic work. Sedimentary sequences hitherto regarded as 'non-magnetic' are now open to detailed examination with the aim of locating oil- and gas-bearing structures. Remote-sensing methods utilizing airborne measurement of infra-red and ultraviolet radiation and radar echoes from rocks to identify their composition from the air are being investigated, and already these measurements are being made from spacecraft.

But the advent of the digital computer has undoubtedly had, and will continue to have, the most profound effect on geophysics. Besides greatly speeding up the tedious process of data reduction, which has become almost automatic from field digital recording to final map production, the computer enables the mass of raw data to be analysed to derive hitherto inaccessible information. Already in seismic reflection work, velocity data for depth conversion is obtained by computer analysis of the field records. Further developments envisaged are systems in which the geophysicist can modify his field shooting programme on the basis of interpretations carried out in a few minutes in the field by a transportable high-speed digital computer. The 'man-machine discourse' concept will be developed whereby the processed records can be reviewed on-line to the computer, and the geophysicist can interrogate the computer to find the effect of changing the processing parameters or of using a different processing sequence. Machine-picking of reflections on seismic sections and three-dimensional conversion of the seismic sections to true depth sections will also contribute towards obtaining a more accurate picture of underground rock structures and formations.

69

Acknowledgements

The writer acknowledges with gratitude assistance in the preparation of this booklet given by colleagues in the Geophysical and Geochemical Divisions of the Institute of Geological Sciences, by Mr. Eric Pickles of Geophysical Service International Limited and by Mr. David Boyd of Hunting Geology and Geophysics Limited. We are also grateful to the many manufacturers and users of geophysical equipment who have supplied information and photographs. All but a few of the diagrams were drawn by Miss P. M. Devereux of the Museum Design Department.

Printed in England for Her Majesty's Stationery Office
by McCorquodale & Co. Ltd, London

Dd 147243 K.40